Enquete Commission "Protecting the Earth's Atmosphere"
of the German Bundestag (ed.)

Climate Change – A Threat to Global Development

Climate Change –
A Threat to
Global Development

Acting Now to Safeguard the Future

First Report submitted by the 12th German Bundestag's Enquete
Commission "Protecting the Earth's Atmosphere"

Economica Verlag, Bonn
Verlag C. F. Müller, Karlsruhe

Die Deutsche Bibliothek – CIP-Einheitsaufnahme

Climate change — a threat to global development:
acting now to safeguard the future / [Enquete Commission "Protecting the
Earth's Atmosphere" of the German Bundestag (ed.). Transl. into Engl. by:
Wolfgang Fehlberg and Monica Ulloa-Fehlberg]. – Bonn: Economica Verl.;
Karlsruhe: Müller, 1992
    Dt. Ausg. u.d.T.: Klimaänderung gefährdet globale Entwicklung
    ISBN 3-87081-382-2 (Economica Verl.)
    ISBN 3-7880-9849-X (Müller).
NE: Fehlberg, Wolfgang [Übers.]

Cover picture by: ZEFA

Translated into English by:
Wolfgang Fehlberg (aiic) and Monica Ulloa-Fehlberg

1992 Economica Verlag GmbH, Bonn

Typeset and printed by: Bonner Universitäts-Buchdruckerei

Illustration, Graphics and Reproduction: Maryse Forget and Robert
Fontner diGraph GmbH

ISBN 3-87081-382-2 (Economica Verlag, Bonn)
ISBN 3-7880-9849-X (Verlag C.F. Müller, Karlsruhe)

This book was printed on 100% recycled paper.

Preface

A Chance for the Future

Six months after its establishment, the Enquete Commission "Protecting the Earth's Atmosphere" herewith submits its first report, which is a comprehensive, scientifically founded study of up-to-date research findings on the greenhouse effect, the destruction of the ozone layer, and the imminent threat of a climate catastrophe. With the present report, the Enquete Commission "Protecting the Earth's Atmosphere" is continuing the work initiated by its predecessor.

This report gives evidence of the urgent need for suitable measures designed to contain the increasingly manifest climate change. Recent scientific findings, which are described in the present report, confirm what was suspected initially: our planet Earth is warming at an increasing rate. The first signs of climate change are already measurable and noticeable. Hence, there is no reason any more to delay urgently required actions.

For this reason, the first report of the Enquete Commission "Protecting the Earth's Atmosphere" not only provides a detailed account of the latest findings, but it also – and primarily – recommends actions designed to reduce energy-related trace gas emissions at national and international level. In addition, the Enquete Commission proposes an international approach aimed at resolving the conflict between the environment and development, and it submits an overall strategy for the protection of the Earth's atmosphere.

At international level, the Enquete Commission's proposals – i.e. reducing carbon dioxide emissions by between 20 and 25 percent at EC level, by 30 percent in all economically strong industrialised nations, and by an average of 20 percent in all industrialised nations by the year 2005 – will require major interventions in national and international energy policies. In order to put these proposals into practice, it will be necessary to convince the other countries concerned of the necessity of adopting such far-reaching reduction targets, and – as quickly as possible – to work out

V

corresponding international agreements in order to ensure that an internationally coordinated and harmonised approach is adopted in this matter. The time left to arrive at such far-reaching and detailed international agreements is very short. This applies in particular to the "United Nations Conference on Environment and Development" which will be held in Rio de Janeiro. For this reason, the Enquete Commission "Protecting the Earth's Atmosphere" is submitting recommendations for action which appear to be an adequate means to establish at least a basis for an international climate protection policy in the framework of this conference.

I hope that the German Federal Government will adopt the Commission's recommendations and initiate corresponding measures at national level, and that it will present and defend the Commission's proposals at international level.

Only if people all across the world become aware of the danger that our planet is exposed to will we have a chance to ward off this global threat. The present report is intended as a contribution towards mastering this great challenge. With a view to the "United Nations Conference on Environment and Development" to be held in Rio de Janeiro, it is at the same time an urgent appeal – an appeal addressed to political decision-makers and the international public at large to find, and embark upon, new paths towards international cooperation and reorganising North/South relations. Only if we succeed in resolving the conflict between the environment and development in a way that satisfies all the parties involved – and in a manner that is in harmony with nature – will humanity have a future worth living for.

I am greatly indebted to the President of the German Bundestag for the kind support which she has given to the Commission. I would also like to thank all the members of the Commission for their intensive cooperation. And last but not least, I would like to commend the secretariat – personally and on behalf of the Commission – for their untiring and exemplary efforts, as well as for their excellent cooperation in a spirit of mutual trust.

Bonn, 31 March 1992

Dr. Klaus W. Lippold, MP
Chairman of the Enquete Commission
"Protecting the Earth's Atmosphere"

Composition of the Enquete Commission "Protecting the Earth' Atmosphere"

Members

Dr. Klaus W. Lippold (Offenbach), MP (CDU/CSU)
chairman

Dr. Liesel Hartenstein, MP (SPD)
deputy chairman

Herbert Frankenhauser, MP (CDU/CSU)
Klaus Harries, MP (CDU/CSU)
Dr. Peter Paziorek, MP (CDU/CSU)
Trudi Schmidt (Spiesen), MP (CDU/CSU)
Bärbel Sothmann, MP (CDU/CSU)
Brigitte Adler, MP (SPD)
Prof. Monika Ganseforth, MP (SPD)
Horst Kubatschka, MP (SPD)
Dr. Klaus Kübler, MP (SPD)
Martin Grüner, MP, former parliamentary secretary (F.D.P.)
Marita Sehn, MP (F.D.P.)
Dr. Klaus Dieter Feige, MP (BÜNDNIS 90/DIE GRÜNEN)

Prof. Dr. Wilfrid Bach
Prof. Dr. Dr. Rudolf Dolzer
Dr. Ing. Alfred-Herwig Fischer
Prof. Dr. Hartmut Graßl
Prof. Dr. Klaus Heinloth
Prof. Dr. Peter Hennicke
Prof. Dr. Hans-Jürgen Jäger
Prof. Dr. Eckart Kutter
Prof. Dr. Klaus Michael Meyer-Abich, former minister
Prof. Dr. Hans Michaelis, former director-general
Prof. Dr. Wolfgang Seiler
Prof. Dr. Alfred Voss
Prof. Dr. Ing. Carl-Jochen Winter

Secretariat

Roland Jacob (Director)
Michael Bisek
Klaus Hanfland
Harald Kesberg
Dr. Kora Kristof
Dr. Christiane Paulus
Dr. Martin Rieland
Ralf Schmidt
Manfred Treber
Wilhelm Bauer
Elke Greif

Table of Contents

X

New Findings and Recommendations for Action

The current status of scientific findings on the impact of human activities on the greenhouse effect, as well as on the associated global climate change and its potential consequences, and on stratospheric ozone depletion, can be summarised as follows:

(1) First signs of climate change are now manifest

Observations made in the past 30 to 50 years clearly suggest that the global climate is beginning to change. This is demonstrated by the following observations which corroborate each other:

- tropical ocean surface temperatures have increased by 0.5 °C;
- there has been an increase in tropospheric water vapour concentrations above the tropics;
- in the mid-layers of the tropical troposphere, there has been a rise in the amount of bound heat released;
- the temperature gradient between the equator and polar latitudes has grown;
- mean wind velocities have increased;
- the quasi-stationary low pressure areas above the northern Atlantic and northern Pacific Oceans have increased in depth.

Today's global mean temperature ranges about 0.7 °C above the 1860 level. In the same period of time, the mass of inland glaciers in the Alps has decreased by about 50 percent.

(2) In the past few years, scientific knowledge about the man-made greenhouse effect has been strengthened by a growing body of evidence

In the past few years, scientific understanding of the man-made greenhouse effect has steadily improved. Man-made increases in the concen-

1

trations of long-lived greenhouse gases – i.e. carbon dioxide, methane, nitrous oxide and chlorofluorocarbons – continue unabated. The most important man-made greenhouse gas is carbon dioxide, whose current tropospheric mixing ratio is 355 ppmv, which is higher than at any other time during the past 160,000 years. Carbon dioxide accounts for 50 percent of the man-made greenhouse effect, while methane accounts for 13 percent, tropospheric ozone for 7 percent, nitrous oxide for 5 percent, all CFCs for 22 percent, and stratospheric water vapour for 3 percent of this phenomenon.

In the next 100 to 200 years, the increases in the atmospheric concentrations of man-made greenhouse gases will have a much greater impact on the climate than any other factor, such as volcanic eruptions or changes in the intensity of solar radiation. Except for some remaining questions regarding the relative importance of the contribution of clouds, the key internal feedback mechanisms in the climate system are now understood. It is very likely that the equivalent CO_2 concentrations will double as early as during the first half of the next century. This will further accelerate the rise of the global mean temperature (to a level of 0.3 °C per decade), and it will intensify changes in spatial and temporal rainfall distribution.

(3) The most important causes are emissions from the energy sector, as well as from agriculture and deforestation

Most radiatively active trace gases are still released in the energy sector (including transport). They, alone, account for about half of the global warming potential. Due to the political changes in Eastern Europe and in the former Soviet Union, a completely new situation has emerged, particularly in the energy sector. This is reflected in the fact that, for one thing, there has been a marked decline in energy demand in these countries because of the restructuring of the former centrally planned economies; on the other hand, the end of the East/West conflict will permit closer cooperation between Western and Eastern European countries. This will offer an opportunity to achieve substantial improvements in energy efficiency, and hence, reductions of CO_2 emissions. Against the background of these developments, a review of the predictions with regard to medium-term trends in global energy consumption appears to be necessary. In this context, it should also be borne in mind that the transport sector's share of energy consumption will increase because of more intensive cooperation between the East and the West, and because of the advent of the Single European Market.

The trace gases released as a result of tropical deforestation account for about 15 percent of the greenhouse effect. Their impact on regional climatic conditions is even more pronounced. In the past decade, the deforestation rate in tropical forests has increased to a total of 170,000 square kilometers annually, i.e. by 50 percent. In addition, there is a risk now that boreal forests will also suffer from large-scale deforestation.

Worldwide, agriculture accounts for about 15 percent of the emissions of radiatively active trace gases, with CO_2, CH_4 and N_2O being the major substances involved. The main sources of CO_2 releases are biomass burning, the conversion of forests into farmland, and secondary fires used to preserve areas. Agricultural sources of methane emissions are rice paddies, cattle feedlots and biomass burning, and another source is sanitary landfills. N_2O not only adds to the greenhouse effect, but it also contributes to ozone depletion. Since N_2O is formed due during the decomposition of nitrogen compounds in soils, nitrogen fertiliser is a major contributor towards these emissions. Since climate change will have a direct impact on agriculture, it will be necessary to adopt more environmentally sound, "low-emission" farming methods in future.

(4) Man-made stratospheric ozone depletion is much more advanced than had been assumed up to a few years ago

Man-made stratospheric ozone depletion is much greater than had been assumed up to a few years ago. Ozone losses are most pronounced during the winter and spring months (about 6 percent per decade). This increase, which represents an acceleration of the trend by another 2 percent per decade as compared to previous analyses, is due to the greater ozone depletion observed during the Eighties. In terms of its depth and its expanse, the 1991 Antarctic ozone hole was comparable to the ozone holes observed in 1987, 1989 and 1990.

In the winter of 1991–92, an unusually low total ozone abundance was measured over large areas of the Northern Hemisphere; in Europe, the ozone levels measured in the months of December, January and February were up to 10 percent below the long-term mean.

Current findings suggest that all chemically induced ozone losses are due to the stratospheric abundance of chlorine and bromine compounds. The overwhelming part of the increase in stratospheric concentrations of these two elements is caused by man-made emissions.

It is expected that the ozone trends observed will continue to speed up in the next few decades. An immediate phase-out of CFC production is therefore indispensable.

3

(5) Preliminary studies on possible associated effects demonstrate the potential threat involved in this global climate change

Major progress has been achieved in assessing regional threat potentials. There is a risk that the climate change will have a greater impact on the countries of the South than on the industrialised nations.

The most direct threat emanates from an increasing frequency of climatically induced catastrophes (e.g. tropical cyclones), which has already become manifest. In future, there will also be a much higher frequency of droughts alternating with heavy rainfall, which will mainly jeopardise semi-arid regions.

The expected rise in sea level by between 70 and 100 cm during the next century will increase the number of catastrophic floods and lead to permanently flooded fertile coastal plains, some of which are densely populated. Deltas and estuaries of large rivers will be particularly at risk in this context. In addition, some Pacific island states will suffer considerable losses of land, and there is a risk that parts of these island states will become uninhabitable.

Both the extent and the rate of climate change will overtax the adaptability of forests and natural ecosystems. There is a risk that ecosystems will collapse on a large scale, which will have severe ecological and socio-economic consequences.

Agricultural production will be particularly jeopardised by climatic shifts. It is above all in continental climates that soils can be expected to dessicate, which will lead to corresponding degradation phenomena (e.g. increasing salinity, erosion). An increasing frequency of extreme climatic events and greater proliferation of plant diseases and pests in a warmer climate will have an adverse impact on yields. However, the fertilising effect associated with increasing atmospheric CO_2 concentrations will hardly affect plant growth. Against the background of rapid population growth, there is a risk that world food supply will be severely compromised.

Another climatically induced threat may be an acceleration of microbial decomposition of dead organic matter in a warmer climate. The additional atmospheric carbon dioxide emissions caused by this phenomenon might reach a magnitude that would be comparable to the emissions due to the combustion of fossil fuels, which might substantially enhance the greenhouse effect.

(6) Time to act

The new scientific findings presented above have increased the pressure on the international community of nations to take action. With a view to

4

the "United Nations Conference on Environment and Development", and considering the hearing held in January 1992 on the topic of the status of international political decision-making by the German Bundestag's Enquete Commission "Protecting the Earth's Atmosphere", it cannot be expected that it will be possible to reach a full-scale consensus on the fundamental objectives (cf. Chapter 6.1) within a short period of time.

It is with this in mind that the Commission has drawn up the recommendations specified below. The Commission feels very strongly that these recommendations are minimum requirements with regard to the outcome of the negotiations which will take place in the next few months.

(1) Our knowledge about man-made climate change has now reached such a high level of certainty that gaps in knowledge can no longer be cited as a reason to refrain from initiating preventive political measures. Wherever governments delay actions designed to reduce emissions of radiatively active substances, this cannot be justified by gaps in knowledge. The international community of nations is called upon:

  – to avert, as much as possible, the threat of climate change,
  – to share in solidarity the adverse effects of the climate change that can no longer be averted.

(2) The need for further research with regard to the foreseeable climate change is not contested. While the current status of scientific knowledge already justifies substantial emission reductions, additional future knowledge may make corresponding action necessary. Current gaps in our knowledge mainly refer to the following issues:

  – the accuracy of climate predictions,
  – regional differences in climate change and its impact,
  – the economic as well as the more drastic social effects of climate change in the various countries, in particular with regard to food supply,
  – the effects on the other parts of the biosphere.

The international community of nations is called upon to close the remaining gaps in our knowledge and to take additional action in accordance with new findings.

(3) Most of the currently foreseeable climate change has so far been caused by the industrialised nations. Their current economic system cannot be generally applied because of its impact on the climate; if it was copied by the developing countries, this would increase the risks of ecological catastrophes. The international community of nations is

called upon to identify and implement climatically sound economic systems where it will no longer be possible for any country to benefit at the expense of other countries, future generations or the natural environment. A first step in that direction should be the adoption of the polluter-pays principle (common, but differentiated responsibility) at international level.

(4) It will be above all the Third World countries that will have to suffer from the foreseeable climate change. While climate policy – for the time being – is mainly a task of the industrialised nations because they are the main polluters, the climate crisis must not be aggravated by the future development of countries which are not yet industrialised. Above and beyond current development cooperation, preserving the climatic conditions of life will therefore be a key factor in any future development policy. Poverty must not be perpetuated for the sake of preserving the climate; it will require a new strategy which will have to combine preventive measures to protect the climate with efforts aimed at overcoming poverty. The international community of nations is called upon to search for new policies to be pursued by industrialised nations and developing countries in order to ensure development that is acceptable for all countries in terms of its climatic soundness. These policies must be designed to secure common survival, and they must offer all countries a chance of sustainable development.

(5) This change in the orientation of the global ecological and economic development should be initiated at the "United Nations Conference on Environment and Development". The discrepancies between the industrialised nations and developing countries are so large that only small steps will be possible as long as the industrialised nations consume a disproportionately high share of the goods of the Earth. In the final analysis, however, it is in the interest of all the parties concerned if at least the following steps are taken in Rio de Janeiro for the purpose of vigorously pursuing the process aimed at developing an effective international climate policy.

(a) The international community of nations should agree immediately after the Conference to enter into negotiations on a protocol designed to lay down specific reduction targets for emissions of radiatively active substances.

(b) The protocol to be adopted at the end of these negotiations should be based on the current status of scientific findings.

(c) The protocol should be reviewed in previously defined intervals in order to reflect the progress in climate change and in scientific findings.

(d) All the climatically relevant scientific research findings that are accessible to the countries which are parties to the protocol should immediately be evaluated and made available internationally.

(6) The global objective set by the 1988 Toronto Climate Conference was to reduce global emissions of radiatively active substances by 20 percent by the year 2005 and by 50 percent by the middle of the next century. The validity of this demand is strongly backed up by recent findings. The international community of nations is called upon generally to confirm the objective defined in Toronto, irrespective of which reduction rates will be allocated to specific countries.

(7) The conference in Rio de Janeiro should already lead to concrete agreements reflecting the immediate political will of all the countries represented to take seriously measures designed to protect the climate. In accordance with the polluter-pays principle, it is primarily the industrialised nations which are called upon to initiate concrete steps to introduce an effective global climate policy. The developing countries will be unable to make their contributions without support from industrialised nations; in fact, they will need both technological and financial assistance.

In Rio de Janeiro, it will be necessary to conclude agreements which set out the required new approaches towards cooperation and towards accomodating the conflicting interests of the industrialised nations and of the developing countries, and which form a platform for common action. In view of the urgency of this matter, the participants in Rio de Janeiro should not content themselves with adopting general and incomprehensible declarations. Instead, they should agree on ways of immediately initiating the institutional, financial and technological cooperation which will be needed in future between the industrialised nations and the developing countries, thereby facilitating subsequent negotiations on a climate convention.

- For this purpose, the international community of nations is called upon – as far as institutional cooperation is concerned – from now on to accept the Global Environmental Facility (GEF) not only as a pilot concept but as a permanent institution. The decision-making structure of the GEF will have to changed in such a way that it will be acceptable for all countries, including the developing countries; hence, in terms of its substance and the procedure adopted, it can set an example for a novel type of environmental partnership. In this context, the experience with the Multilateral Fund of the Montreal Protocol should serve as a model.

- In the field of financial cooperation, the industrialised nations are called upon to make substantial increases in their contributions to the GEF – at least by a factor of 3 – up to the entry into force of a climate convention. The funds to be made available for this purpose should not be obtained by reducing other environmental expenditure. The German Federal Government is called upon to declare its readiness to adopt such an approach jointly with all the other industrialised nations.

- The Commission proposes that a limited so-called "Green Fund" (climate fund) should be established to supplement the GEF. This "Green Fund" should be used to finance all those environmental projects which, under the current agreements, are covered by neither the GEF nor the Multilateral Fund of the Montreal Protocol.

- In order to initiate and promote the process of technological cooperation between the North and the South as early as at the conference in Rio de Janeiro, it is desirable to reach preliminary agreements in this field, as well.

  (a) Upon the request of developing countries, the resources of the GEF should be used to promote studies aimed at describing and defining the potential future contributions of specific countries and regions in the South towards a global climate policy. These studies should be carefully conducted in cooperation between the country concerned, the GEF and external experts. It is essential that these studies should address not only the technological capacities that are present now and needed in future; instead, they should also deal with human resources issues such as training, know-how and management.

  (b) At the same time, the GEF should draw up inventories of the latest technologies which can contribute towards reducing greenhouse gas emissions in the various countries and regions concerned, in as cost-effective a manner as possible.

  (c) On the basis of the country reports and the inventory list to be drawn up, the countries represented in the GEF should decide which technologies should be promoted in the various countries and regions; in this context, cost/benefit ratio considerations should play the key role.

  Conceivable instruments of implementation at national and international level – such as taxes, levies, voluntary restraint commitments, as well as cooperation and compensation instruments (joint implementation) – whose usefulness will have yet to be established, should be applied if they support the objectives of the convention. Where necessary, the rules of GATT and of the World Bank should be adapted to this regime.

(8) The common objective of preventing catastrophic global climate change can only be attained if individual countries demonstrate on their own initiative that this objective can be achieved and how it can be achieved. The Federal Republic of Germany has undertaken to reduce CO_2 emissions by at least 25 percent (relative to 1987 levels) by the year 2005. Other countries are following suit. The international community of nations should call upon all countries possessing the necessary economic, technological and political prerequisites not to wait for the adoption of a climate convention and its implementation protocols; instead, they should immediately start preparing and implementing effective national and regional measures designed to protect the climate.

1 Principles and Objectives of a Global Policy Designed to Protect the Earth's Atmosphere

The Threat to the Climate is a Global Challenge for Humanity

We are about to witness climate change of a magnitude which has been unprecedented in past millenia. The greenhouse effect and the destruction of the protective ozone layer have assumed alarming proportions. Both these phenomena confront humanity with a challenge of unprecedented magnitude.

Unlike past threats to the environment, what we are now facing is a global threat whose local and regional impact can hardly be predicted yet. Atmospheric concentrations of greenhouse gases – above all carbon dioxide, but also CFCs, methane, nitrous oxide and ozone-forming substances – are on the rise, thereby accelerating the rate of global warming. When confronted with this problem, tried and tested solution strategies such as the use of repair techniques to remedy local environmental problems are bound to fail. Hence, completely new approaches will have to be identified and developed, i.e. we will have to part with traditional approaches. For the sake of prevention, it is indispensable that we should initiate far-reaching measures to protect the Earth's atmosphere as soon as possible. This will require contributions not only from politics, science and industry, but also from each individual citizen.

The imminent climate change is evidence of the fact that the wasteful use of resources by the industrialised nations of the North has reached its limits. Only if we achieve a change in thinking and move towards an ecologically and socially oriented market economy will it be possible to prevent the impending catastrophe. Numerous problems in the world which have been on the agenda for a long time without any solution in sight – particularly the population explosion, poverty, hunger, underdevelopment and the energy issue – are inseparably linked and interact with the imminent climate catastrophe. We must not lose any more time. Some problems have already assumed dimensions that leave hardly any room for successful solutions. If our planet Earth is to be preserved for future generations, noble words must now be followed by deeds. The United Nations Conference on Environment and Development in Rio de Janeiro could become a landmark in this respect.

If there is no growing awareness of the impending disaster on the part of citizens and politicians, and if there is no increasing readiness to accept and support drastic measures in industry and in agriculture, both in the North and in the South, there is little hope of finding a feasible solution. It is only if all the parties involved realise that they are jointly exposed to the same immediate threats – albeit to varying degrees – that we can hope for any improvement. Only then will it be possible for a comprehensive political will to develop, and hence cooperation, which is a prerequisite to the survival of all of humanity. With its present report, the Enquete Commission "Protecting the Earth's Atmosphere" would like to support the political decision-making process required.

Climate Change and Its Effects

– Man-made global warming

There is only one conclusion that can be drawn from current scientific evidence: the increasing warming of the Earth's atmosphere is caused by man-made emissions. For the past two decades, scientists have issued urgent appeals warning against the catastrophic consequences of rising temperatures. By now, there is scientific proof showing that their concern was justified. The greenhouse effect was initially a natural phenomenon which made life possible at all on our planet. Owing to the natural concentrations of atmospheric gases such as water vapour, carbon dioxide, ozone, nitrous oxide and methane, the Earth's mean surface temperature has been raised from $-18\,°C$ to a tolerable level of $15\,°C$. However, since the beginning of industrialisation, the original concentrations of these gases have increased substantially due to human interventions. Rapid increases have been observed mainly in the abundance of trace gases – particularly carbon dioxide, methane and nitrous oxide – whose atmospheric concentrations have risen sharply since the industrial revolution. The main sources of these emissions are the combustion of large amounts of fossil fuels in the energy and transport sector, deforestation and the use of intensive farming methods. In the early thirties of this century, emissions of radiatively active trace gases assumed a new quality. Up to the time when they were first produced in industry, greenhouse gases such as CFCs and halons had not been present in the environment. The destructive effect which they have on the stratospheric ozone layer and on the warming of the lower atmosphere represents a

11

particularly acute potential hazard, once again caused exclusively by human activities.

According to climatologists, these emissions of greenhouse gases have been responsible for the 0.5 °C rise in mean temperature observed in the past 100 years. The effects of this rise in temperature are already noticeable today. Tropical ocean surface temperatures, for instance, have increased significantly since 1950, thereby increasing atmospheric water vapour concentrations by between 10 and 20 percent. In addition, the temperature differences between the tropics and higher latitudes have become more pronounced. As a result of these changes, there has been an increase in wind velocities by between 5 and 10 percent, and of wind energy by between 10 and 20 percent. This has led to an increase in the frequency of cyclones, in particular in the tropics, some of which have had catastrophic effects.

It is feared that what we have seen so far have been only the effects of emissions released 30 or 40 years ago. So, without man being able to exercise any influence whatsoever, current greenhouse gas emissions will intensify climate change and its adverse effects in the next few decades.

At present, the atmospheric concentration of carbon dioxide – which accounts for about 50 percent of the additional, man-made greenhouse effect – continues to rise at an alarming rate. Never before in the past 160,000 years have atmospheric carbon dioxide levels been as high as they are today. Unless drastic control measures are adopted, the equivalent carbon dioxide concentration in the atmosphere can be expected to increase to 550 ppm by the year 2030, which would be twice as high as the pre-industrial level. Meanwhile, current scenarios paint dismal pictures of the effects to be expected. If a "wait-and-see" approach is adopted, atmospheric temperatures will increase by between 2° and 5 °C by the year 2100. This drastic temperature rise which will be unprecedented – in terms of both its magnitude and its rate of development – will have extremely severe socio-economic and ecological effects of hitherto unpredictable dimensions.

– *Rise in sea level*

In the past 100 years, global warming has led to a rise in sea level by approx. 10 to 20 cm. Should this trend persist, the sea level can be expected to rise by between 70 and 100 cm by the end of the next century, due to not only the thermal expansion of ocean water but also the melting of continental glaciers. Because of this sea level rise, many coastal regions and islands will disappear under the water masses; millions of people will have to leave their homes for good, coastal cities and fertile land will be flooded, and groundwater reservoirs in coastal regions will be salinised. In this context, the lowlands of Egypt, Bangladesh, Thailand, China, Brazil, Indonesia and Argentina are particularly at risk. In addition, there are numerous groups of islands such as the Maldives, as well as the delta regions of the Nile, the Ganges and the Amazon, which are equally at risk if the sea level rises.

– Changes in rainfall

Rising temperatures will lead to changes in wind circulation, which will affect global rainfall distribution. Overall, rainfall volumes will grow with increasing temperatures and evaporation rates. However, changes in rainfall frequency and intensity will vary widely from region to region. This, in turn, will have a major impact on vegetation, as well as on productivity in agriculture and forestry. This impact will be further intensified by soil desiccation due to increased evaporation.

– Natural ecosystems

Natural ecosystems will be particularly affected by rising temperatures and changing rainfall and evaporation patterns. Climate change will lead to a poleward shift in global vegetation zones. In fact, a temperature rise by as little as 1 °C will cause a shift by about 200 km. Since most ecosystems will not be able to adjust to the predicted global warming rate of 0.3 °C per decade, there is a risk that they will collapse. In many regions, this effect will be aggravated by the fact that, in view of the high proportion of farmland areas, the range of alternative areas for natural ecosystems to move to is extremely limited.

– Agriculture

This might lead to problems of unprecedented magnitude for agriculture. Due to increasing global warming, there will be shifts in cultivation zones. Plant growth will be jeopardised by changes in rainfall distribution, increases in UV-B radiation, and changes in the atmosphere's chemical composition. Food supply, which is already problematic in many parts of the world as it is, will become yet more difficult in future. It is in particular the countries of the South which will be at risk – countries whose economies are highly dependent on agricultural production. The regions concerned include countries such as Brazil, Peru, as well as the Sahel, South-East Asia and the Asian parts of the CIS and China. These areas already suffer from a lack of suitable land, capital, technological know-how and adequate producer prices.

Ozone Depletion

Apart from adding to the greenhouse effect, CFC emissions deplete the ozone layer. In addition, after being attacked by CFCs and other aggressive chemical compounds, the ozone layer is no longer sufficiently able to act as a shield protecting all creatures on Earth from the deleterious UV-B radiation.

Increasing UV-B radiation will have severe effects on human health, animals, terrestrial plants and marine biocenoses. Drastic increases in the incidence of skin cancer and of eye lesions are just some of the predicted effects on human health. Hence, it can be assumed that the risk of developing skin cancer or eye lesions will increase substantially. In the course of the next few decades, increasing UV-B radiation can be expected to damage plant and animal life. In addition, if marine planktion is damaged, this may have a severe impact on the food chain in the oceans. Increasing UV-B radiation will thus reduce the amount of carbon stored both in the terrestrial biomass and – more importantly – in the oceans, thereby further enhancing the greenhouse effect.

Threat and Opportunity

Findings to date suggest that the poorer countries in the tropical and subtropical regions will mainly be affected if no adequate control measures are initiated. The consequences will be hunger, misery and endless streams of environmental refugees. Those affected will need the solidarity of those that will have been spared. They will also be a threat to world peace. After the peaceful settlement of the East/West conflict, there is now a risk that there will be massive conflicts between the North and the South as a result of the climate catastrophe. Population migration from flooded or desiccated areas, or from areas that are exposed to such risks, and resettlement elsewhere, might well turn out to be the most alarming consequence of climate change. The industrialised nations may also be subject to considerable repercussions and social upheavals.

The environmental problems caused by the man-made greenhouse effect are further aggravated by the depletion of the ozone layer, the damage done to forests by air pollutants, and the increasing pollution of the oceans. Immediate action is required if the imminent catastrophe is to be averted. It is already too late to prevent this alarming development altogether. Even if drastic emissions cuts were implemented immediately, global warming would continue. Because of their high heat storage capacity, the oceans delay warming of the Earth's surface and of the lower atmosphere by between 30 and 40 years. In other words: temperatures will continue to rise even if all emissions of greenhouse gases are stopped immediately. It is only with a certain delay – after 30 or 40 years – that the full impact of the man-made greenhouse effect will be felt. Many greenhouse gases have an atmospheric lifetime of about 100 years. Even if their emission rates could be "frozen" at their current levels, their concentrations would continue to rise in the following 100 years. Immediate action is indispensable if environmental damage is to be limited to a bearable minimum.

Emissions of radiatively active trace substances (including aerosols) will have to be reduced as soon as possible; the production of CFCs, and of partially halogenated substitutes and halons will have to be stopped; and an end will have to be put to the destruction of forests – not only in tropical regions but also in temperate and boreal zones – because forests play a vital role as carbon dioxide sinks.

The impending climate catastrophe represents both a threat and an opportunity. It is true that humanity has manoeuvred itself into a dangerous situation by ruthlessly exploiting nature. However, the need to change direction, to put more emphasis on the ecological component in the system of the market economy, and the need to build up a new relationship between the North and the South – one that is geared towards accomodating conflicting interests – at the same time represent a great opportunity. The threat of a climate catastrophe might contribute towards a breakthrough for a new type of development policy. The "United Nations Conference on Environment and Development" in Rio de Janeiro will be a milestone on the way towards a more equitable world. Even if it is not possible to solve all the problems at this conference, it at least offers an opportunity to pave the way for a new relationship between the North and the South, and to prepare the ground for an international approach towards coping with the imminent climate catastrophe. There has hardly ever been a better time than today to change direction. Due to the changes in the geopolitical situation which have come about because of the settlement of the East/West conflict and because ideological conflicts have been overcome, there are now new options and opportunities for political action – options and potentials which should be utilised for global cooperation in the interest of solving the problem of environment and development.

The Rationale for Global Action

The climate catastrophe which is looming at the horizon will affect our planet as a whole. The environmental damage to be expected will no longer be limited to specific regions or local sites; instead, its effects will jeopardise all of humanity. Every single country on Earth is more or less involved in the destruction of our common resources – and hence, the

15

prerequisites to our survival. At the same time, every country will also be affected by the impending climate catastrophe. In the final analysis, this development is due to inadequate human behaviour, and hence, it will not be possible to cope with this development unless there are major changes in behaviour. The industrialised nations and the developing countries share common – albeit different – responsibility for the behaviour which causes climate change and for the associated problems.

– Costs and benefits involved in action and no action

If we fail to take action in order to control the impending global climate catastrophe, the price we would have to pay – in the medium and long-term – for the short-term benefits of not acting would be high, indeed. For if we fail to act, this would mean: maintaining our current standard of living; no expenditure incurred for the development of energy efficient technologies which help to conserve resources; no price increases for products that are harmful to the climate, etc. On the other hand, the consequential costs involved would include damage in agriculture and forestry caused by temperature and rainfall changes; expenditure incurred for the construction of dams because of the rising sea level; and adverse effects on human health brought about by increasing UV-B radiation.

Despite this alarming scenario, the speed at wich emissions of radiatively active substances are being curtailed falls far short of what is required. The impending climate change is a global problem which can only be solved by means of joint international efforts. For economic reasons, the developing countries are unable to initiate – by themselves – effective measures designed to protect the climate. Instead, they have to concentrate on other problems such as the population explosion, poverty, hunger, etc.

For this reason, it is indispensable for new political mechanisms (conventions, international treaties, etc.) to be developed in order to establish a new platform for the relations between the industrialised nations and the developing countries. A common North/South strategy must be aimed at satisfying the basic needs of the population living in developing countries, and it must be aimed at setting off a development process which closes the gap between the developing countries and the industrialised nations in an environmentally sound manner.

It will not be possible to attain the objective of an internationally harmonised climate policy unless the parties involved agree on an "equitable" distribution of the burdens and benefits of this strategy.

16

In this context, the industrialised nations bear a special responsibility. The imminent climate change is mainly due to pollution which they have caused. Because of their economic and technological lead, the industrialised nations are in a position to work towards an internationally harmonised and effective climate protection policy.

If the developing countries are to be integrated in an international climate policy, it will be necessary for the industrialised nations to stop their wasteful use of resources, and to set an example in this field. In addition, the developing countries will have to receive transfers to be used in climatically relevant areas. Intensive technological and economic cooperation between the developing countries and the industrialised nations will be equally indispensable.

At first glance, the most striking effect of a climate protection policy is the costs incurred, e.g. increases in the prices of resources whose use has adverse effects on the climate, as well as the costs involved in energy conservation, and the research expenditure needed to develop new, adapted technologies. However, this view neglects the fact that investments in climate protection can open up new national and international markets for a variety of different economic sectors, including small craft establishments which carry out thermal insulation jobs, research institutes which help utilise the technical and economic potential of renewable energy sources, and also large corporations which might develop new technologies for optimising the transport sector.[1]

---

[1] **For the record: Statement by Prof. Dr. P. Hennicke**
Conservative estimates based on studies conducted by the EC (Directorate-General XII (1)) and by F. Krause et al. (2), as well as specific studies on buildings (3), renewable energy sources (4) and the electricity sector, suggest that, if an active energy policy is pursued and if corresponding general conditions are established by government, reducing CO_2 emissions by about 30 percent by the year 2005 in the Federal Republic of Germany will not pose any insurmountable problems for German industry or with regard to financing. In fact, extensive energy efficiency and co-generation potentials are cost-effective because they should be utilised anyway for economic reasons, since – in addition to bringing relief to the environment and protecting the climate – they help save microeconomic and macroeconomic costs. In a study conducted by the Directorate-General XII (5), for instance, the authors have come to the conclusion that in ten EC countries, energy conservation potentials in the fields of lighting, household appliances, buildings (due to better thermal insulation) and transport, are economically attractive: the energy conservation investments are more than offset by the energy cost reductions achieved. According to this EC study, the costs of reducing CO_2 emissions by 30 percent in the Federal Republic of Germany (old federal states only) would amount to only 0.48 percent of the gross national product.

Literature:
(1) European Community, Directorate-General XII, 1991
(2) Krause et al., 1992
(3) Ebel et al., 1990
(4) Nitsch, Ziesing, 1991
(5) European Community, Directorate-General XII, 1991.

Any economic assessment of climate protection measures will have to include their impact on the highly complex economic cycle as a whole. Not only the direct effects but also the indirect effects will have to be taken into account. Climate policy can be managed in an intelligent and low-cost manner. Whenever there is a need for renovation, for instance (e.g. in old buildings), thermal insulation could automatically be included in order to minimise the costs of climate protection measures. Hence, there will not only be economic losers if a climate protection policy is pursued in a given country, but there will also be winners.

The costs involved in climate protection measures will have to be weighed against both the macroeconomic benefits and the damage prevented by such a climate policy.

The current problem does not only affect the present generation. We – who will be the first to bear the costs of the climate protection measures adopted – will have to pay not only for what we have done ourselves, but also for the failings of earlier generations and for the well-being of future generations. The survival of our children and our children's children can be safeguarded only if we act today.

Our generation cannot shirk its responsibility with regard to the imminent climate change and its consequences.

– Responsibility of the industrialised nations

The industrialised nations have a special responsibility to bear. Techno-logical progress has brought about an increase in the standard of living and the quality of life for many people in the industrialised nations, and it has mitigated the various forms of poverty prevailing there. However, this prosperity has had to be bought at the price of high levels of consumption of energy and natural resources, and at the price of environmental destruction. The destruction of natural resources still persists, and emissions from industrial production, energy supply and transport continue to rise.

The exploitation of nature is not a coincidence. Instead, it is due to the fact that there is no adequate price for the use of the environment in today's economic systems. No ecological criteria are applied when we make use of nature, exploiting its mineral wealth and consuming its natural resources. The damage done in the process is not taken into account, neither in our planning of economic decisions nor in our cost accounting.

The industrialised nations account for three quarters of the emissions and activities which currently jeopardise the global climate. If the developing countries copied the behaviour of the industrialised nations, this would

18

merely accelerate the collapse of our environment. About 95 percent of all carbon dioxide emissions, which occur during the combustion of fossil fuels and which are mainly responsible for today's global warming, have been caused by the industrialised nations of the North – cumulatively over the past 100 years. Technological achievements of industrial production, which for a long time were regarded as symbols of progress, have turned out to be potential hazards as well. CFCs – once celebrated as a major advance and used as refrigerants and as propellants in aerosols – now are mainly known for their adverse effects on the climate.

The developing countries will suffer most from the impending climate change. Agriculture, which will predominantly be affected by this climate change, accounts for a very large proportion of the developing countries' gross national products. Developing countries are least able to help themselves on the basis of their resources; they are already confronted with enormous problems as it is. In absolute terms, these countries will also be most severely affected by the predicted effects of climate change, i.e. rising sea levels, changes in vegetation zones and in rainfall.

– Environment and development

The climate change issue is embedded in the conflict between environment and development. Many of the as yet unresolved global problems – such as the population explosion, underdevelopment, poverty and hunger – are currently escalating, which is also reflected by increasing environmental destruction.

About 80 percent of global energy-related emissions of radiatively active trace gases is currently caused by 15 percent of the world population. Energy consumption in the industrialised nations of the North has settled at a very high level. As far as the other contributory factors are concerned, the industrialised nations are also mainly responsible for the change in our climate, while the developing countries' role in this climate change is currently relatively minor. Their per-capita energy consumption is a fraction (between about $1/10$ and $1/40$) of what it is in the industrialised nations. However, the developing countries are as much entitled to enjoy development and quality of life as the industrialised nations. Even if the increase in energy consumption can be kept much smaller in the developing countries today than during the early years of industrialisation in today's industrialised nations, it is still foreseeable that, in future, the developing countries – as they follow the industrialisation path of the industrialised nations on their way towards development – will play a much greater role with regard to the change in our climate. This will considerably aggravate today's problems.

The growing impact of the developing countries on the change in our climate would be due not only to their industrialisation progress. The destruction of the environment in the developing countries, as well as tropical deforestation and the conversion of deforested areas into farmland, are all due to poverty. Since there are no other affordable fuels and no working energy supply systems, forests are cut down in order to obtain firewood as a free source of energy. The situation is dramatically aggravated by the population explosion currently observed in these countries. As a result, the environment will increasingly be overused.

Scientific and technological progress in the industrialised nations tends to accentuate the economic differences between the rich and the poor countries, and it tends to make it more difficult to introduce technological innovations.

The developing countries' position in world trade is relatively weak. World market prices for their commodities are rather low. In addition, their poverty increases continuously because of their high foreign debts, decreasing foreign investment in developing countries, and a substantial net capital outflow from the poor to the rich countries. The gap between the North and the South is becoming wider. Unless the developing countries are given a fair chance of development, it will be impossible to stop the destruction of natural resources and tropical deforestation. Our economic system and our lifestyle, both of which are not sufficiently geared towards preserving the prerequisites to our survival, pollute not only to our environment and jeopardise the survival not only of our future generations but also of those of the developing countries.

If the global climate catastrophe is to be averted, it will be necessary for the industrialised nations to reduce their disproportionately high pollution of the environment as quickly as possible, and for the developing countries to overcome their misery and poverty in an ecologically sustainable manner by achieving their own development, in keeping with their traditions and the conditions prevailing in their countries.

In their justified desire to satisfy the basic needs of their population and to close the prosperity gap between the industrialised nations and the developing countries, the latter have so far mainly been guided by the industrialised nations' economic system which has already led to global over-utilisation of resources.

Many countries are already so highly indebted that it seems unlikely that they will be able to find a solution by themselves. It is the duty of the industrialised nations to help the developing countries – which have contributed substantially to the prosperity of the North – in their endeavours to achieve development in harmony with the environment.

– Eastern Europe

The collapse of the political systems in the East revealed the full scope of environmental destruction in Eastern Europe. In the East – as in the West – smokestacks for a long time were regarded as signs of industrialisation and the modern age, while environmental protection was long stigmatised as being unproductive. One of the reasons for the ruthless consumption of natural resources was the tough ideological competition with the West's highly mechanised industrial societies for geopolitical supremacy. Funds were invested in unproductive sectors such as the armaments industry. Because of the lack of capital, the manufacturing sector therefore had to operate with obsolete technical plants. In the technically highly obsolete power stations, energy was produced by means of fuels which in some cases contained high levels of pollutants. Where high-risk technologies were applied, safety standards were neglected. Centrally planned economic systems lead to inefficient economic activities and environmental damage. Neither the environment nor the ecological effects of wasteful energy consumption were taken into account in production plans and economic planning.

The system of subsidising energy proved to be highly harmful for the environment. Over decades, the centrally planned economies favoured heavy industry and their high energy intensity. Governmental energy subsidies and the lack of market-driven prices led to energy wastage and emissions on a large scale. Like the developing countries, the countries of the East will not be able to solve their enormous environmental problems by themselves; they depend on help from the Western industrialised nations.

2 The Current Status of Scientific Findings

Summary

Observations made in the past 30 to 50 years clearly suggest that the global climate is beginning to change. This is demonstrated by the following observations, which corroborate each other:

– tropical ocean surface temperatures have increased by 0.5 °C;
– there has been an increase in tropospheric water vapour concentrations above the tropics;
– in the mid-layers of the tropical troposphere, there has been a rise in the amount of latent heat being released;
– the temperature gradient between the equator and polar latitudes has grown;
– mean wind velocities have increased;
– the quasi-stationary low pressure systems above the northern Atlantic and northern Pacific Oceans have increased in depth.

Today's mean global temperature ranges about 0.7 °C above the 1860 level. In the same period of time, the mass of inland glaciers in the Alps has decreased by about 50 percent.

In the past few years, scientific understanding of the man-made greenhouse effect has steadily improved. Man-made increases in the concentrations of long-lived greenhouse gases – i.e. carbon dioxide, methane, nitrous oxide and chlorofluorocarbons – continue unabated. The most important man-made greenhouse gas is carbon dioxide, whose current mean tropospheric mixing ratio is 355 ppmv, which is higher than at any other time during the past 160,000 years. Carbon dioxide accounts for 50 percent of the man-made greenhouse effect, while methane accounts for 13 percent, tropospheric ozone for 7 percent, nitrous oxide for 5 percent, all CFCs for 22 percent, and stratospheric water vapour for 3 percent of this phenomenon.

A completely new situation has evolved in the energy sector as a result of the political changes which have occurred in Eastern Europe and in the former Soviet Union. This new situation is reflected in the fact that energy demand has substantially declined in these countries because of the restructuring of the former centrally planned economies. Against the background of this development, it seems necessary to revise the forecasts with regard to medium-term trends in global energy demand. In the past two years, global energy-related CO_2 emissions have stagnated as a result of the development described above, in combination with recessionary trends or a slowdown in economic growth in many industrialised nations.

Iraq's invasion of Kuwait once again underlined the unstability of the political situation in the region which possesses by far the world's largest oil reserves. Rapid fluctuations in the price of crude oil were the result of this political crisis.

Since the unification of the two German states, there has been a considerable reduction of CO_2 emissions in the Federal Republic of Germany. This has been due to the fact that production has fallen substantially, as a preliminary consequence of the economic restructuring process going on in the new federal states. Overall, this has led to a reduction of energy-related CO_2 emissions in the Federal Republic of Germany, amounting to about 6 percent between 1987 and 1990, and to some 12 percent (provisional estimate) by 1991.

In the course of time, energy consumption in the transport sector has increased, both in absolute and in relative terms. The transport sector accounts for 27 percent of global energy consumption. In addition, energy consumption in the transport sector is predicted to grow much more rapidly than in any other sector. The pollution caused by the transport sector is mainly due to emissions from private motor vehicles. Emission reductions achieved in this field by introducing technological improvements in the vehicles have not been large enough to compensate for emission increases due to growing traffic volumes.

Trace gas emissions caused by tropical deforestation account for about 15 percent of the greenhouse effect. What is much more important, however, is the impact on the regional climate. In the past decade, the deforestation rate in tropical forests has increased to a level of 170,000 square kilometers per year, or by about 50 percent. In addition, there is a risk now that boreal forests will also suffer from large-scale deforestation.

Worldwide, agriculture accounts for about 15 percent of the emissions of radiatively active trace gases, with CO_2, CH_4 and N_2O being the major substances involved. The main sources of CO_2 releases are biomass burning, the conversion of forests into farmland, and secondary fires used

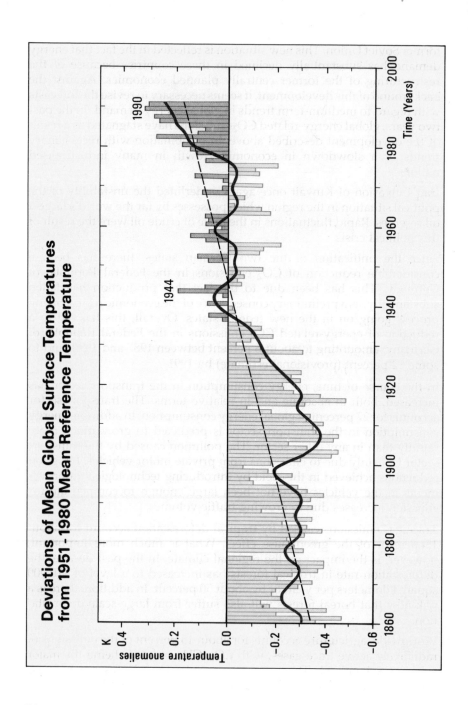

Deviations of Mean Global Surface Temperatures from 1951 - 1980 Mean Reference Temperature

to clear areas of land. Agricultural sources of methane emissions are rice paddies, cattle feedlots and biomass burning, and another source is landfills. N_2O not only adds to the greenhouse effect, but it will also increasingly contribute to ozone depletion if its atmospheric concentration continues to rise. Since N_2O is formed during the decomposition of nitrogen compounds in soils, nitrogen fertiliser is a major contributor towards these emissions. Since climate change will have a direct impact on agriculture, it will be necessary to adopt more environmentally sound, "low-emission" farming methods in future.

2.1 Observed Changes in Climate Parameters

More intensive observations in the recent past have demonstrated that there have been significant changes in a number of important climate parameters, and that, hence, it must be assumed that there is a global change in climate. Some of the important observations made in this context are listed below:

– Time series of mean global and seasonal surface temperatures, which go back to 1860, show that there has been a long-term increase by 0.45 ± 0.15 °C during the past 100 years (see Fig. 2.1). The seven warmest years during this period of time were (in ascending order) 1944, 1989, 1987, 1983, 1988, 1991 and 1990 (maximum to date).

– Temperature changes in the Northern Hemisphere have varied widely, both from region to region and from season to season. Above the Atlantic ocean, for instance, temperatures have risen to a very limited extent, except for tropical latitudes, while temperatures in the northern part of North America and in Sibiria increased more rapidly than the mean global temperature.

– In the past 20 years, there has been a change in the mean diurnal variation of surface temperatures above land surfaces at northern

---

◀ *Fig. 2.1: Anomalies (departures from 1951-1980 reference interval) of mean global surface temperatures; combined air and ocean surface temperatures (columns), smoothed 10-year mean (bold line) and linear trend (dashed line). The mean annual temperature for 1990 is 15.5 °C; the mean temperature given for 1991 is provisional. The linear trend amounts to 0.5 °C (uncertainty: 0.1-0.2 °C); the trend/noise ratio is 2.7. The order of the seven warmest years is: 1990, 1991, 1988, 1983, 1987, 1989, 1944. Source of data: IPCC, 1990, 1992; edited by: Schönwiese (1991, 1992).*

N.B.: For normally distributed data universes, trend/noise ratios of >2 and >3 correspond to a statistical significance of >95 and >99 percent, respectively.

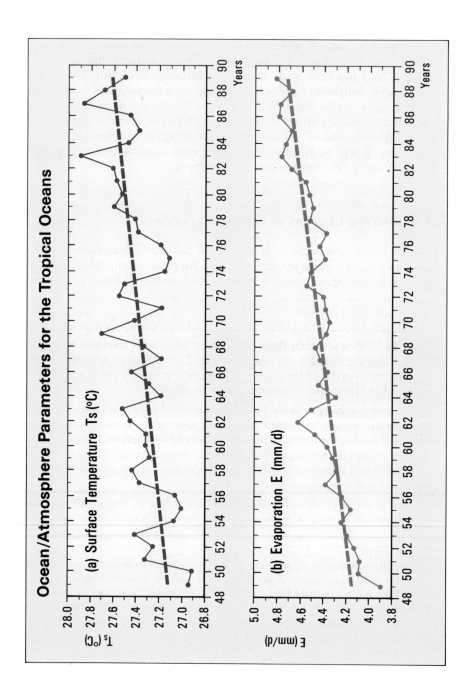

Ocean/Atmosphere Parameters for the Tropical Oceans

(a) Surface Temperature Ts (°C)

(b) Evaporation E (mm/d)

mid-latitudes. In fact, mimimum temperatures have slightly increased, while maximum temperatures have remained unchanged (1). This suggests that there has been reduced long-wave radiation – particularly at night – either because of increasing cloudiness or because of increasing amounts of radiatively active atmospheric trace gases. Since daily maximum temperatures have not undergone the same change, it is more likely that this change has been due to the effects of increasing greenhouse gas concentrations.

- Between 1949 and 1989, tropical ocean surface temperatures increased by 0.5 °C (see Fig. 2.2 a). Water vapour pressure increases exponentially with rising temperatures. In the same period of time, evaporation of water increased by 16 percent (see Fig. 2.2 b). Most of the latent heat which is transported by water vapour is released in the tropics and subtropics by means of condensation and precipitation at cloud level.

- Hence, warming is most pronounced in the middle troposphere (at an altitude of between 3 and 6 km) above the tropics and subtropics. Above the Arctic, however, temperatures are reduced within this range of altitude. It should be pointed out in this context that, apparently, there has not been a major change in tropospheric water vapour concentrations at higher latitudes.

- Because of the different temporal development of temperatures at tropical and northern high latitudes, it must be assumed that there has been an increase in both the temperature and the pressure gradient between the equator and the north pole, and thus an increase in the intensity of atmospheric circulation in the Northern Hemisphere (2).

- In the past twenty years, increases in mean wind velocities have been observed at all latitudes, amounting to 1 ms^{-1} (+20 percent) at surface level in the tropics, and 0.4 m s^{-1} (+9 percent) at mid-latitudes. At 500 hPa (5–6 km altitude), an increase of 0.7 m s^{-1} (+6.2 percent) has been observed at mid-latitudes.

- In the past 22 years, the almost stationary low pressure system near Iceland/Greenland has dropped by 5 hPa during the winter months, while the low pressure system above the northern Pacific Ocean

---

◄ *Fig. 2.2:   Time series of ocean/atmosphere parameters for the tropical oceans (between 10 °S and 14 °N)*
(a) surface temperature Ts (°C)
(b) evaporation E (mm/d)
(from: Flohn, 1992)

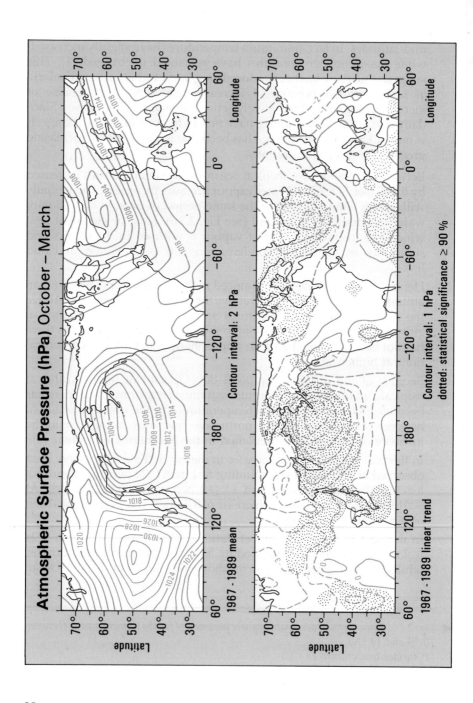

Atmospheric Surface Pressure (hPa) October – March

1967 - 1989 mean
Contour interval: 2 hPa

1967 - 1989 linear trend
Contour interval: 1 hPa
dotted: statistical significance ≥ 90 %

(Aleutian depression) has fallen by 8 hPa (see Fig. 2.3). At the centre of the low pressure system near Iceland, the relative storm frequency increased from 18 percent in 1966–67 to 26 percent in 1988–89. In the Aleutian low pressure system, the storm frequency increased even more: from 17 to 32 percent (1,2).

– An increase in mean wind velocity by between 5 and 10 percent (range applying to the lower layers of the troposphere in the Northern Hemisphere) is tantamount to an increase in wind energy by between 10 and 20 percent. The increase in the storm damage caused, in particular in the past five years (hurricanes "Gilbert" and "Hugo" in 1988 and 1989, respectively; winter storms in Europe in 1987 and 1990; typhoon "Mireille" in 1991), is further evidence of the intensification of general circulation (3).

– Because of the insufficient data base and the wide spatial and temporal variability of precipitation, global estimates of changes in the rates and distribution of precipitation are not very reliable. The data available suggest that there has been an increase in precipitation on the continents by more than 5 percent since 1950, except for the latitude band between 5°N and 35°N, where precipitation has decreased (4, 5).

– The annual snow cover of the continents in the Northern Hemisphere has decreased by about 8 percent since 1973 (1).

– Between 1850 and 1969, the inland glacier volume in the Alps decreased by about 50 percent (Fig. 2.4 [6]). Due to "favourable weather conditions for glaciers" (in particular, relatively low summer temperatures and high-frequency precipitation in the form of snow in summer), most of the Alp glaciers observed continued to expand until about 1983. Subsequently, they decreased in size, so that the data of the 1969 glacier survey are still representative for 1992 (7).

– There is evidence (satellite data) suggesting that the thickness of inland ice is increasing, at least in the southern part of Greenland, probably due to higher precipitation volumes (8). However, these satellite data conflict with observations of a general recession of the glacier tongues in Greenland, which is explained by the increase in temperatures

◄ Fig. 2.3:   Atmospheric surface pressure (October to March) in hPa for the period from 1966-67 to 1988-89 (from: Flohn, 1992)
(a) mean
(b) linear trend

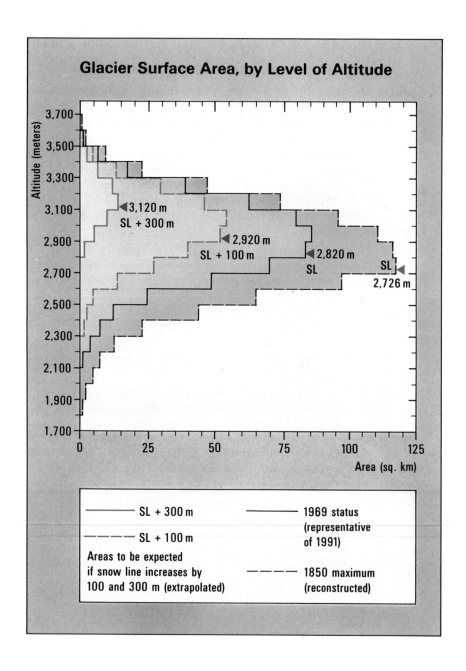

Glacier Surface Area, by Level of Altitude

Altitude (meters)
3,700
3,500
3,300
3,100 ◀3,120 m SL + 300 m
2,900 ◀2,920 m SL + 100 m
2,700 ◀2,820 m SL ◀ SL 2,726 m
2,500
2,300
2,100
1,900
1,700

Area (sq. km)
0   25   50   75   100   125

——— SL + 300 m   ——— 1969 status (representative of 1991)
– – – SL + 100 m
Areas to be expected
if snow line increases by
100 and 300 m (extrapolated)   – – – 1850 maximum (reconstructed)

observed in Greenland in the past hundred years and by the associated melting rate (9). In Antarctica, no temporal trend seems to be manifest.

- Satellite data collected between 1978 and 1987 showed a significant decrease in the extent of sea ice north of Greenland. The mean regional atmospheric temperature rise for this period of time was 0.5 °C.

2.2   Climate and Greenhouse Effect

Before discussing the most recent findings with regard to the relative impact of man-made emissions on climate change, the following paragraphs briefly provide some important physical background information. The term "climate" is used to denote the long-term mean weather conditions prevailing in a given region. The parameters studied to determine mean weather conditions include atmospheric and ocean surface temperatures, radiation, rainfall, soil moisture, as well as the frequency and intensity of extraordinary meteorological events (storms, late frost periods, droughts, etc.). Since the climate is subject to natural variability extending over time scales of a few years up to 100,000 years, time-averaging periods have to cover at least 20 to 30 years and data records at least 100 years if the time trends derived are to be statistically well founded.

An important factor which influences the climate is the radiation budget of the Earth, which is determined by relatively short-wave solar irradiation in the spectral region of visible light and by the longer-wave radiation from the Earth's surface in the infrared region of the spectrum (heat radiation). The actual condition of the climate is controlled – both regionally and globally – by a variety of complex control loops which are coupled with one another (climate system), involving the atmosphere, the pedosphere (i.e. land surfaces), the hydrosphere (mainly the oceans), the

---

◀ *Fig. 2.4:   Altitude distribution of glacier surface areas in Austrian Alps:*
- *1969 status (representative of 1991)*
- *1850 maximum (reconstructed)*
- *surface areas to be expected if snow line rises by 100 and 300 meters (extrapolated)*

N.B.: An increase in temperature by 1 °C corresponds to a shift of a glacier's equilibrium line by about 170 m
(from: Patzelt and Aellen, 1990)

cryosphere (i.e. areas covered by snow and ice, mainly in the polar regions) and the biosphere (i.e. living organisms) on the continents and in the oceans. The processes occurring inside the various control loops and the mechanisms responsible for the coupling of the control loops are still insufficiently understood.

Man intervenes in these control loops by various activities. Since the beginning of the industrial age, man has burnt increasing amounts of fossil fuels and reclaimed large land areas for agriculture, thereby contributing towards sustained changes in the chemical composition of the Earth's atmosphere. This has also changed the greenhouse effect caused by the atmosphere.

The greenhouse effect is due to the action of radiatively active trace gases. Although the mixing ratios of these gases in the Earth's atmosphere are very low, they play a crucial role for the temperature, and hence, for the climate of the Earth. While they allow short-wave solar radiation to reach the Earth's surface unhindered, these trace substances absorb the heat radiated from the Earth's surface, thereby leading to a warming of near-surface air masses. Since the conditions prevailing in a greenhouse are very similar, the effect which radiatively active substances have is often referred to as a "greenhouse effect". If the atmosphere did not contain any radiatively active trace substances, the average surface temperature of the Earth would be $-18\,°C$ – a temperature which would be $33\,°C$ below the current mean temperature of $+15\,°C$.

2.2.1 Radiatively active atmospheric trace gases

In an atmosphere which is not influenced by human activities, the most important radiatively active trace gases are water vapour (H_2O), carbon dioxide (CO_2), methane (CH_4) and nitrous oxide (N_2O). Due to man-made increases in the corresponding emission rates, the concentrations of these trace gases have grown. Together with chlorofluorocarbon (CFC) emissions from industrial processes, these higher concentrations intensify the natural greenhouse effect – a mechanism which is also referred to as the man-made greenhouse effect. The man-made greenhouse effect is further exacerbated by tropospheric ozone which is formed by photochemical processes. Precursors such as CO, NO_x and the group of volatile organic compounds (VOCs), which contribute to the formation of ozone, are referred to as indirectly acting trace gases. Water vapour and carbon dioxide, taken together, currently account for about 85 percent of the overall greenhouse effect (10). Any change in the concentrations of radiatively active trace gases – in particular gases that are optically active within the range of the so-called water vapour window (wavelength range: 8–13 μm) – is bound to change the global climate.

2.2.1.1 Water vapour

In the atmosphere, water is a rather complex dynamic system in which the various states of aggregation – vapour, liquid droplets and ice crystals – constantly interact with each other. In all of these states of aggregation, atmospheric water is radiatively active. The most common form of atmospheric water is water vapour, which accounts for 65 percent of the overall greenhouse effect, and hence, is the most important radiatively active trace gas in the atmosphere.

The hydrological cycle of water vapour, most of which is released into the atmosphere through evaporation of ocean surface water, is relatively short. The mean time span between the evaporation of water and its precipitation in the form of rain or snow is eight days. The hydrological cycle is closely coupled to the atmosphere's general circulation. The rate of evaporation – and hence, the flux of water vapour into the atmosphere – depends on three factors: surface temperature, wind velocity, and atmospheric humidity. Water vapour concentrations are particularly high in near-surface air layers above the warm, tropical oceans. With increasing altitude and proximity to the poles, the water vapour content decreases by more than a factor of 100 and 10, respectively. Relatively low water vapour levels are found in subtropical arid regions which are characterised by descending air movement, and hence, dry air masses.

The heat bound by the evaporation of water (latent heat) amounts to more than three-quarters of the solar energy absorbed by the ocean surface. This heat is released when the water vapour in the atmosphere is transformed into cloud droplets by condensation.

Under current conditions, about 525 billion tonnes of water evaporates per year. A large part of this water vapour is transported to continental regions where it precipitates in the form of rain. Because of its short mean lifetime of water vapour, and because of the temperature-dependence of evaporation rates, its tropospheric concentrations are subject to considerable spatial and temporal variations.

Due to the general warming of the Earth's surface, evaporation has increased, in particular above the tropical oceans (11). This increase in the evaporation rate is a natural response to the man-made greenhouse effect, which is caused by increasing concentrations of the other radiatively active trace gases, and thus intensifies the greenhouse effects of CO_2, CH_4,

33

N_2O, ozone and of the CFCs (positive feedback). On the other hand, it is known that cloud formation is usually associated with rapid, albeit small-scale upward air movement, which for reasons of continuity is compensated for by usually large-scale downward air movement outside the clouds. As a result, large parts of the upper troposphere may "dry out", which would counteract the man-made greenhouse effect (negative feedback). The question as to whether increasing water evaporation rates and increasing surface temperatures will on average wind up being a positive or a negative feedback for the greenhouse effect depends on how vertical water vapour distribution will change in the troposphere and especially how water vapour concentrations will change in the upper troposphere. Recent measurements have shown that, in the upper troposphere, water vapour concentrations have also increased in regions with intensive convection (the tropics) (12). In order to illustrate this point by means of an example, Fig. 2.5 shows the tropospheric water vapour concentrations observed between 1985 and 1989 as a function of altitude and latitude in both hemispheres. The data plotted in this figure represent the differences between July and January concentrations. Seasonal variations are a yardstick of the sensitivity of atmospheric water vapour concentrations to changes in temperature. The data in the figure clearly demonstrate that, in the entire troposphere, water vapour concentrations during the sommer months are higher than during the respective winter months. This also means that the greenhouse effect, which is caused by the "dry" greenhouse gases, is amplified by increasing water evaporation. This positive feedback for the man-made greenhouse effect has also been confirmed by model calculations (13).

However, the effects of the increase in atmospheric water vapour concentrations observed to date go beyond the climatic consequences mentioned above. Due to the increasing vertical transport of water vapour, for instance, more heat of condensation is released in the middle and upper layers of the troposphere. This, in turn, has a direct impact on the atmosphere's general circulation, which is maintained by the differences in energy balance between the equatorial zone and the polar regions (2) (cf. Chapter 2.1 "Observed Changes in Climate Parameters").

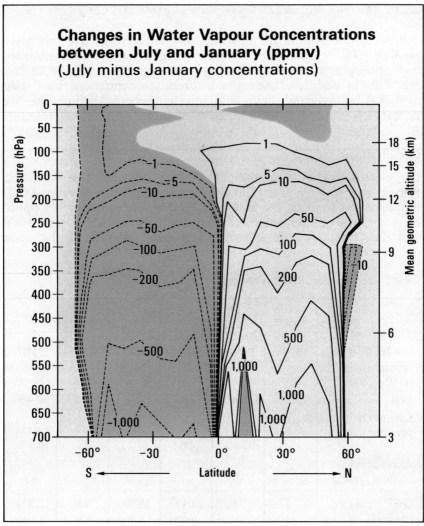

Changes in Water Vapour Concentrations between July and January (ppmv)
(July minus January concentrations)

Fig. 2.5: Changes in water vapour concentrations as a function of altitude and latitude between July and January (calculated from SAGE II satellite data measured between January 1985 and July 1989).
The solid lines indicate the areas in which water vapour concentrations are higher in July than in January. Areas with higher water vapour concentrations in January are indicated by dark blue colour and dashed lines. The figure shows that atmospheric water vapour concentrations are higher during the summer months than during the winter months; i.e. global warming involves higher water vapour concentrations up to the higher layers of the troposphere, thereby further exacerbating the man-made greenhouse effect.
(from: Rind et al., 1991)

2.2.1.2 Carbon dioxide, methane, nitrous oxide and CFCs

Following water vapour, the most important radiatively active trace gases are CO_2, CH_4, N_2O and CFCs. Since the beginning of industrialisation, their atmospheric concentrations have risen steadily (see Table 2.1 and Fig. 2.6). In addition, tropospheric ozone concentrations have also increased, however, only in the Northern Hemisphere. All these gases are primary contributors to the additional, man-made greenhouse effect.

Carbon dioxide (CO_2)

CO_2 is the second most important radiatively active trace gas following tropospheric water vapour. The mean tropospheric mixing ratio of CO_2 has increased from its pre-industrial level of 280 ppmv to 355 ppmv currently, or by 25 percent. Never before in the past 160,000 years have CO_2 concentrations been at such a high level. At present, the mean

Table 2.1: Characteristics of Atmospheric Trace Gases

	Carbon dioxide	Methane	CFC-11	CFC-12	Nitrous oxide	Ozone [2]
Mixing ratio ...	ppmv	ppmv	pptv	pptv	ppbv	ppbv
Pre-industrial (1750—1800) ...	280	0.8	0	0	288	5—15
1991	355	1.74	280	484	311	30—50
Rate of change per year	1,8 *(0.5%)*	0.015 *(0.75%)*	9.5 *(4%)*	17 *(4%)*	0.8 *(0.25%)*	0.15 *(0.5%)*
Atmospheric lifetime (years) .	50—200	10	65	130	130—150	0.1
GWP (mol.)[1] ..	1	21	12,400	15,800	206	2,000
GWP (kg)[1]	1	58	3,970	5,750	206	1,800
Percentage share[1]	*50*	*13*[3]	*5*	*12*	*5*	*7*

[1] GWP (mol.): global warming potential (GWP) relative to the same volume of CO_2 (mol.)
   GWP (kg): GWP relative to the same mass of CO_2 (kg)
   Percentage: percentage shares of the various greenhouse gases in the man-made greenhouse effect during the 1980s.
[2] All data are very rough mean values since tropospheric concentrations vary widely in terms of space and time.
[3] Includes direct effects only.

tropospheric mixing ratio of CO_2 is increasing by 0.5 percent annually, or by between 1.6 and 1.8 ppmv. If this trend persists, CO_2 will reach a level of about 450 ppmv by the year 2050. The atmospheric lifetime of man-made CO_2 is long; depending on whether the deep sea and the terrestrial biosphere are taken into consideration as carbon reservoirs, and depending on how they are weighted, the lifetime of CO_2 is estimated to be between 50 and 200 years (10,1). Despite an uneven geographical distribution of sources and sinks, the horizontal and vertical distribution of tropospheric CO_2 is relatively even. The CO_2 mixing ratio is subject to annual variations which are controlled by the terrestrial biosphere and which are particularly pronounced in the Northern Hemisphere. Maximum concentrations are reached in spring, while minimum levels are found in autumn.

An important point, which until recently had not been sufficiently taken into consideration in connection with the carbon cycle, is the fact that there is a small but clearly identifiable CO_2 gradient between the Northern and the Southern Hemisphere. In the eighties, this gradient amounted to about 3 ppmv. However, model calculations which are based on the well-known geographical distribution of CO_2 emissions from the combustion of fossil fuels and on a relatively even global distribution of CO_2 sinks suggest that the interhemispherical gradient amounts to 5 ppmv. This discrepancy may point to the existence of a substantial CO_2 sink (2–3 Gt C per year) in the Northern Hemisphere (14).

The authors of two recently published studies, in which this point was taken into account and which also made use of other ·data from observations, came to two totally different conclusions with regard to the relative role of the terrestrial biosphere as compared to that of the hydrosphere (oceans):

The analysis of Tans, Fung and Takahashi (15) was based on measured data about the regional atmosphere/ocean CO_2 flux in the northern Atlantic and Pacific Oceans. By extrapolating the data, the authors then arrived at a carbon balance for the oceans in the Northern Hemisphere, showing a net CO_2 absorption of less than 0.7 Gt C per year north of 15° northern latitude. This relatively low value was interpreted as evidence suggesting that there was a CO_2 sink of 2 Gt C per year in the terrestrial biosphere at northern mid-latitudes.

In their analysis, Keeling, Piper and Heimann (16) took into account not only the north/south gradient of tropospheric CO_2 but also the corresponding gradient of the $^{13}C/^{12}C$ isotopic ratio in CO_2. This isotopic ratio is determined primarily by the relative contributions of CO_2 from fossil and from recent biological sources. After evaluating the data available,

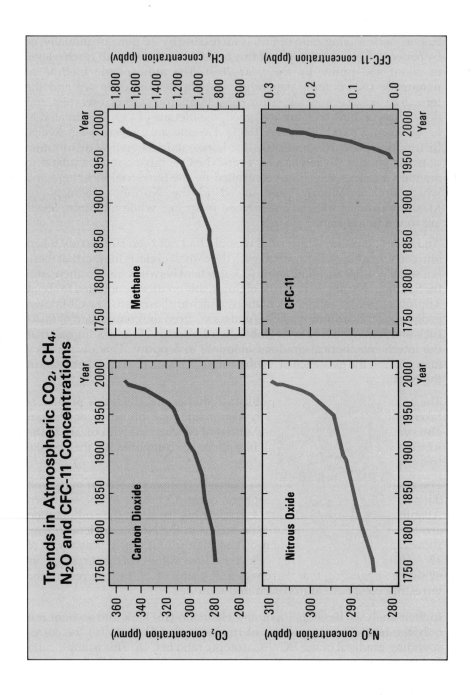

Trends in Atmospheric CO₂, CH₄, N₂O and CFC-11 Concentrations

Keeling et al. precluded the existence of a predominant biospheric CO_2 sink in the Northern Hemisphere.

Apart from these conflicting conclusions, observations have shown that the increase in the mean tropospheric CO_2 mixing ratio is less rapid than model calculations had predicted (1). This might also be due to the fact that the absorption capacity of the oceans may have been underestimated. These discrepancies illustrate the fact that a large part of the global CO_2 cycle is not yet understood.

Methane (CH₄)

Methane (CH₄)

Atmospheric CH_4 is a trace gas which affects the climate both directly and indirectly. Its mean tropospheric mixing ratio has now reached a level of 1.74 ppmv, which is more than a factor of 2 above the pre-industrial level of 0.8 ppmv. The highest tropospheric CH_4 mixing ratios are found in the Northern Hemisphere, where the mean hemispheric concentration is 1.78 ppmv, while the mean concentration in the Southern Hemisphere amounts to 1.70 ppmv. Like CO_2, CH_4 is subject to pronounced annual variations in the troposphere, with a maximum reached in spring and a minimum observed in autumn. These annual variations are determined by temporal variations in the magnitude of both CH_4 sources and sinks. The magnitude of sinks is determined by seasonal variations in tropospheric OH radical concentrations.

Atmospheric methane is produced by several sources on the Earth's surface, whose magnitude is still poorly understood. Vaghjiani and Ravishankara (17) have recently demonstrated that the rate of CH_4 reactions with atmospheric OH radicals had been overestimated by up to 25 percent. Since these reactions are the primary sink of atmospheric CH_4, the estimates of the magnitude of the sources had to be revised accordingly (18). The atmospheric lifetime of CH_4 is now estimated to be 10 ± 2 years.

Between 1962 and 1979, the mean tropospheric mixing ratio of CH_4 increased by about 1 percent annually. In the past few years, the rate of increase has slowed down to about 0.8 percent per annum (19, 20, 21). This may be due to a reduction of emissions from both natural and man-made sources. However, a more likely explanation would be an increase in CH_4 decomposition due to a presumable increase in tropospheric OH radicals, mainly in the Northern Hemisphere (1).

◄ *Fig. 2.6: Trends in atmospheric CO_2, CH_4, N_2O, and CFC-11 concentrations since 1750. What is striking is the accelerated increase in the concentrations of all gases after about 1950.*

Source: IPCC WG I

Because of its role in photochemical ozone formation, CH_4 has an impact on the tropospheric oxidation potential, which in turn affects the concentrations and the distribution of other radiatively active trace gases, and hence, indirectly affects the radiation budget. Due to its oxidation in the stratosphere, atmospheric CH_4 is also a major contributor to water vapour forming at these altitudes, and thus has an impact on the greenhouse effect. These indirect contributions of CH_4 are estimated to amount to about two-thirds of the direct contributions (1). In this context, the vertical distribution of ozone and water vapour have been taken into consideration, both of which are particularly active near the cold tropopause.

Nitrous oxide (N_2O)

Atmospheric N_2O concentrations are currently rising at a rate of 0.8 ppbv per year. The mean global tropospheric mixing ratio of N_2O now (1991) amounts to 311 ppbv. The atmospheric N_2O cycle, and in particular the capacities of the various sources and sinks, are still poorly understood. Estimates based on the still highly imprecise data available to date suggest that the N_2O sinks – including N_2O accumulation in the atmosphere – have an overall capacity of about 20 million tonnes per year, while total N_2O source capacity is estimated at merely 8–19 million tonnes per annum (22). This leads to one of two possible conclusions: either the global potential of the currently known N_2O sources has been underestimated, or there are other, additional sources that have not yet been taken into account in the atmospheric N_2O budget.

Halogenated hydrocarbons

Halogenated hydrocarbons are among the radiatively active trace gases with the highest global warming potentials, due to their high radiative activity and their long atmospheric lifetimes. There are no natural sources for fully halogenated hydrocarbons (CFCs) and for most partially halogenated hydrocarbons (H-CFCs). These hydrocarbons, which are exclusively of industrial origin, are released into the atmosphere either directly (e. g. when they are used as cleaners or aerosol propellants) or with a certain delay (e. g. when products containing CFCs or H-CFCs are scrapped). Atmospheric mixing ratios of hydrocarbons have been rising rapidly. This applies both to the CFCs (e. g. CFC 11, 12, 113) – which are not decomposed until they reach the stratosphere where they are photodissociated – and to the H-CFCs (e.g. H-CFC-22), most of which are destroyed by photochemical processes while they are still in the troposphere. Only methyl chloride (CH_3Cl), methyl bromide (CH_3Br) and methyl iodide (CH_3I) have natural sources (oceans, biomass burning).

In addition to being radiatively active, the CFCs and their related brominated compounds (e.g. halon 1211) are precursors of reactive chlorine and bromine, and hence, they contribute to the increasingly rapid depletion of the stratospheric ozone layer. Reactive bromine is particularly dangerous since its ozone depletion potential is between 30 to 120 times higher than that of reactive chlorine. In this context, heterogeneous chemical processes occurring on the surfaces of stratospheric particles (aerosol particles and ice clouds) are particularly important because they accelerate ozone depletion. Heterogeneous reactions are also believed to be responsible for development of the Antarctic "ozone hole".

By 1990, the mean stratospheric mixing ratio of reactive chlorine formed in the stratosphere by photodecomposition of halogenated compounds had reached a level of 3.3 ppbv; it is expected to continue to increase to a level of 4.1 ppbv by the year 2000, if CFC production is not phased out more rapidly than required under the Montreal Protocol (2nd meeting of the Parties to the Protocol 1990 in London), and if H-CFC-22 emissions are allowed to increase at a rate of 3 percent annually between 1990 and the year 2000 without any further substitution of H-CFCs for CFCs. Under these conditions, ozone losses in the Nineties can be expected to be comparable to what they were in the Eighties. However, this will be true only if there are no major changes in the heterogeneous ozone depletion in the stratosphere. However, increasing levels of stratospheric sulphate particles suggest that stratospheric ozone depletion will accelerate. This increase in sulphate particles is due to two phenomena: as a short-term effect, the injection of larger amounts of sulphurous gases during the recent eruption of the Pinatubo; and as a more long-term consequence, the increase in so-called stratospheric background aerosols, caused inter alia by air traffic in the lower stratosphere.

Model predictions suggest that the emission reductions agreed upon will not lead to a return of current stratospheric chlorine concentrations to the level measured before the emergence of the Antarctic ozone hole (2 ppbv) before the second half of the 21st century (23). The natural background mixing ratio of chlorine, which is mainly determined by CH_3Cl emissions from the oceans, currently amounts to about 0.6 ppbv (10).

Table 2.2 shows the mean tropospheric mixing ratios and growth rates of selected halogenated hydrocarbons, as well as their ozone depletion and global warming potentials.

Table 2.2: *Mixing Ratios and Trends of Various CFCs, H-CFCs and Other Compounds, as well as Their Ozone Depletion and Global Warming Potentials*

		Mixing ratio (pptv)	Annual growth rate (pptv)	(%)	Lifetime (years)	Ozone Depleting Potential[1]	Global Warming Potential[2]
CFC-11	CCl_3F	280	9—10	4	65	1	3,500
CFC-12	CCl_2F_2	484	17—18	4	130	0.9	7,300
CFC-13	$CClF_3$	5	—	—	400	—	—
CFC-113	$C_2Cl_3F_3$	60	6	10	90	0.8—0.9	4,200
CFC-114	$C_2Cl_2F_4$	15	—	—	200	0.6—0.8	6,900
CFC-115	C_2ClF_5	5	—	—	400	0.3—0.4	6,900
CCl$_4$		146	1—1.5	1.5	50	1.0—1.2	1,300
H-CFC-22	$CHClF_2$	122	5—6	7	15	0.04—0.06	1,500
CH$_3$Cl		600	—	—	1.5	—	—
CH$_3$CCl$_3$		158	4—5	4	7	0.13—0.16	100
halon 1211	CB-ClF_2	1.7	0.4—0.7	12	25	3.0	—
halon 1301	$CBrF_3$	2.0	0.2—0.4	15	110	7.8	5,800
CH$_3$Br		10—15	—	—	1.5	—	—

[1]) The ozone depletion potential was calculated by means of two-dimensional models, using CFC-11 as a reference.
[2]) The global warming potential is integrated over a period of 100 years, relative to the same mass of CO_2 (kg).

Sources: IPCC WG I, 1992
Third report of the Enquete Commission on "Preventive Measures to Protect the Earth's Atmosphere"

2.2.1.3 Ozone (O_3)

For various reasons, O3 plays a special role in the group of radiatively active trace gases. First of all, ozone is a highly reactive compound, and hence, very short-lived (lifetime: 2–3 months in the free troposphere; 1–2 days at surface level). Secondly, ozone is an important precursor compound of OH radicals which play a major role in many photochemical processes, and hence, are very important for the chemical composition of the troposphere. Ozone is one of the gases which has no (direct) sources on the Earth's surface; it is formed exclusively by photochemical processes in the atmosphere (in the stratosphere, mainly by photodecomposition of molecular oxygen; in the troposphere, by photodecomposition of NO_2). The temporal trends in O_3 concentrations in the stratosphere are completely different from tropospheric ozone trends. While stratospheric ozone concentrations have been decreasing, tropospheric O_3 levels have been rising, at least in the Northern Hemisphere. The total ozone in the atmosphere (90 percent of which is in the stratosphere and 10 percent in the troposphere) acts as a filter for penetrating UV radiation from the sun, and thereby has made it possible in the first place for life to develop on the continents of the Earth. Tropospheric ozone, on the other hand, has toxic effects on human health, on animals and on plants, even at relatively low concentrations (≥ 60 ppbv).

Stratospheric ozone

About 90 percent of total atmospheric ozone is found in the stratosphere, where O_3 is produced by photodecomposition of molecular oxygen and subsequent recombination of the oxygen atoms formed with molecular O_2. The stratospheric ozone layer has substantially decreased in the past 20 years. Considerable O_3 losses have been observed mainly at middle and high latitudes of both hemispheres (23) (24), while there has been virtually no chan.ge in ozone concentrations in the tropical stratosphere. O_3 losses vary with the seasons: they are most pronounced during the winter and spring months, and they are somewhat lower during the summer months. Table 2.3 shows the ozone trends which have recently been determined for the period between 1979 and 1991. A comparison of these data with earlier analyses suggests that stratospheric ozone losses have increased by nearly a factor of 2. This is mainly due to ozone depletion in the lower stratosphere, at an altitude of between 13 and 25 km (at mid-latitudes), where local ozone losses of up to 10 percent per decade have been observed. At the same time, stratospheric mean global temperatures have decreased by 0.3 °C per decade (23).

Table 2.3:   Trends in Total Atmospheric Ozone, 1979–1991
            (percentages per decade) (23)

	45 °S	Equator	45 °N	26°–64°N Dobson etc.
	TOMS-data			
December to March	−5.2	+0.3	−5.6	−4.7
May to August	−6.2	+0.1	−2.9	−3.3
September to November	−4.4	+0.3	−1.7	−1.2

The dynamic chemical models of the atmosphere which are currently available can explain only part of these substantial ozone losses. This may be due to one of two reasons:

– low-ozone, chemically perturbed air masses are transported from polar to mid-latitudes, which is not adequately simulated by the models, or

– the heterogeneous chemical processes which occur on the surfaces of sulphate aerosols in the global stratosphere and which contribute to ozone depletion are much more effective than has been assumed to date (25, 26).

Dramatic stratospheric ozone losses were observed during the spring months above Antarctica where this led to the development of the so-called Antarctic ozone hole. The data recorded in October 1991 (23) revealed a minimum vertical column density of 110 Dobson units, which corresponds to a 60-percent ozone loss as compared to the long-term mean for this time of the year (up to the end of the Seventies). Vertical O_3 column densities below 200 Dobson units are now found in an area extending over 16 million square kilometers, which corresponds to about 6.5 percent of the total area of the Southern Hemisphere.

On the other hand, stratospheric ozone losses during Arctic winter are much lower. Model calculations suggest that there are geographically limited O_3 losses of about 10 percent (mini-holes) over a period of one month. Data obtained by direct measurement were also in this order of magnitude.

For further details about stratospheric ozone depletion, see Chapter 3.1.

Tropospheric ozone

Tropospheric ozone concentrations are a function of ozone input from the stratosphere and photochemical ozone formation in the troposphere itself. Stratospheric ozone reaches the troposphere by air mass exchanges between the troposphere and the stratosphere at middle and high latitudes of both hemispheres. This transport mechanism is particularly pronounced during spring in the Northern Hemisphere. In addition, tropospheric ozone is also formed by photochemical oxidation of CO, CH_4 and volatile organic compounds (VOCs) in the troposphere, providing that the NO_x mixing ratio is greater than 10 pptv. In this context, reactive VOCs play an important role as regards the O_3 formation within the Earth's boundary layer (bottom layer of the troposphere), while the long-lived trace gases CO and CH_4 are important for the formation of O_3 in the free troposphere. If the NO_x mixing ratio drops below a level of 10 pptv, ozone production turns into ozone depletion.

Because of the relatively short atmospheric lifetime of O_3, the uneven geographical distribution of its sources, as well as the relatively short lifetimes of its precursors NO_x and VOCs, and because of the highly variable intensity of solar radiation, tropospheric O_3 mixing ratios vary widely from region to region. These variations are dependent on longitude and latitude, as well as altitude and season. In non-polluted air masses in the Northern Hemisphere, O_3 mixing ratios vary between 30 and 50 ppbv, with distinct peaks in spring and summer. Under "smog" conditions in polluted air masses, O_3 mixing ratios can reach levels of more than 100 ppbv. Ozone mixing ratios are usually much lower in the tropics than at northern mid-latitudes. However, this does not apply to the dry season, during which substantial O_3 precursor emissions are caused by large-scale biomass burning. Above the regions concerned, O_3 mixing ratios may be as high as above mid-latitude industrialised regions during summer. On the other hand, O_3 mixing ratios may drop to levels of 4–12 ppbv in unpolluted continental and maritime air masses in the tropics (10).

Fig. 2.7 shows the annual variations of O_3 mixing ratios at mid-latitudes for both hemispheres. It is worth noting the differences observed during the summer months. The most likely explanation for these interhemispherical differences is that man-made percursors have a major impact on photochemical O_3 formation in the Northern Hemisphere.

Since industrialisation, mean ozone mixing ratios in near-surface air masses in the Northern Hemisphere have increased from between 5 and 15 ppbv (27) to their current level of between 40 and 50 ppbv. At northern

45

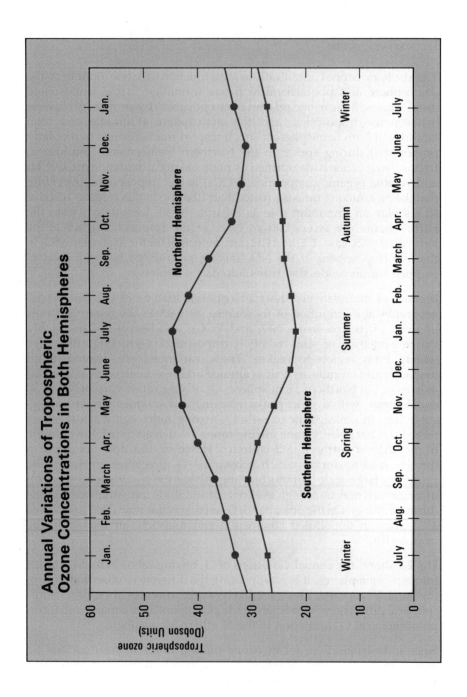

Annual Variations of Tropospheric
Ozone Concentrations in Both Hemispheres

mid-latitudes, the O_3 mixing ratio in the free troposphere has increased by an average of about 1 percent annually over the past 20 years (23).

Effects of ozone on the radiation budget

Man-made changes in vertical ozone distribution call for a differentiated assessment of the associated effects on the radiation budget. Ozone depletion in the lower stratosphere leads to an increase in outgoing long-wave radiation of the surface/troposphere system (negative greenhouse effect) and at the same time to a temperature decrease in the lower stratosphere because of the reduced absorption of solar radiation. The latter has led to a mean global decrease in stratospheric temperatures by 0.3 °C per decade (23).

On the other hand, the increase in tropospheric ozone concentrations (as well as ozone depletion in the upper stratosphere) exacerbates the greenhouse effect. This mechanism is particularly effective if O_3 mixing ratios increase in the very cold upper troposphere. Aircraft emissions play an important role in this context.

Since ozone depletion is latitude-dependent (see above), the man-made greenhouse effect has also become latitude-dependent. While no full-scale climate model calculations have been performed yet on this question, preliminary results obtained by means of one-dimensional models suggest that the cooling effect caused by stratospheric O_3 losses at northern mid-latitudes is somewhat greater than the warming effect brought about by increasing tropospheric tropospheric O_3 concentrations. The additional greenhouse effect due to man-made CFC and H-CFC emissions in the troposphere may also not be quite sufficient to compensate for the cooling effect at these latitudes (28). However, this should not lead to the conclusion that the climate change induced by CFCs and their decomposition products has a compensatory effect because it involves a novel, highly latitude-dependent perturbation of the radiation budget.

◀ Fig. 2.7: *Annual variations of tropospheric ozone concentrations at mid-latitudes in both hemispheres (between 35° and 45°). For the sake of clarity, the two annual profiles are plotted in a staggered manner, with an offset of 6 months between them. (from: Fishman, 1992)*

2.2.1.4 Indirectly acting radiative trace gases

In addition to atmospheric trace gases that have a direct radiative impact, there are a number of other gaseous compounds which indirectly affect the radiation budget of the surface/atmosphere system by changing ozone concentrations in the troposphere and in the stratosphere, affecting the distribution and concentration of OH radicals, or by triggering the formation of additional aerosol particles.

These indirectly acting radiative trace gases usually have atmospheric lifetimes of less than three months. Hence, their concentrations vary widely in terms of both space and time; and in view of the short series of measurements performed to date, it is not possible to make any firm statements about the global trends of their atmospheric mixing ratios.

Carbon monoxide (CO)

Tropospheric CO has a lifetime of between one and three months. Tropospheric CO mixing ratios reach a maximum in spring and a minimum in early autumn. In the Northern Hemisphere, CO concentrations range between 100 and 150 ppbv in less polluted air masses, while levels of between 40 and 80 ppbv have been measured in the Southern Hemisphere (29). In big cities and industrial agglomerations, much higher mixing ratios (between 1 and 10 ppmv) are reached for short periods of time (10). In the troposphere above densely populated areas and in the stratosphere, CO mixing ratios decrease with increasing altitude. In clean-air regions in the Northern Hemisphere, there is a less rapid decrease in tropospheric CO concentrations with altitude. In the Southern Hemisphere, CO seems to be vertically well mixed in the troposphere. Because of seasonal variations, the interhemispherical difference in CO mixing ratios is particularly pronounced in April.

CO emissions are produced by a variety of different sources on the Earth's surface and released into the troposphere. In addition, CO is also formed by photochemical oxidation of methane and VOCs. About 60 percent of total global net CO production, which is estimated at 2,400 million tonnes, is due to human activities. The most important CO sink is the reaction with OH radicals, which account for the decomposition of about 2,100 million tonnes of CO per year. To a lesser extent, CO is also decomposed by microbial processes in soils. A small fraction of CO reaches the stratosphere where it is quickly transformed into CO_2 by oxidation (10).

The available data obtained by measurements suggest that tropospheric CO concentrations are on the rise in the Northern Hemisphere. Their annual rate of increase is estimated to be about 1 percent. No distinct trend has yet been identified in the Southern Hemisphere (1).

Nitrogen oxides (NO and NO₂)

NO and NO_2 are highly reactive nitrogen oxide compounds. Usually, both trace gases are jointly referred to as "NO_x" (nitrogen oxides) because, in the daytime atmosphere, a (photochemical) equilibrium develops very quickly between the two compounds. Because of the very short tropospheric lifetime of NO_x (only about one day) and because of the complex distribution of sources and sinks, tropospheric NO_x concentrations vary widely in terms of both time and space. The lowest NO_x mixing ratios (less than 1 pptv) have been found in extremely clean maritime air masses, while NO_x mixing ratios in polluted air (e.g. above Europe and the eastern part of North America) reach levels of more than 10 ppbv. NO_x concentrations measured in the free troposphere above the Earth's boundary layer range from below 20 pptv (in unpolluted air) to over 5 ppbv (above densely populated areas of highly industrialised countries) (10).

Tropospheric NO_x is produced by various sources on the Earth's surface and released almost exclusively as NO. Based on the data available, some of which are still rather unreliable, global NO_x emissions are estimated at about 50 million tonnes of nitrogen (N) per year, with man-made sources accounting for about 60 percent of these emissions. The greatest single source of NO_x is combustion (combustion of fossil fuels and burning of biomass). Aircraft emissions of NO_x – limited almost exclusively to the upper troposphere and the lower stratosphere – are of particular importance in this context. The indirect radiative impact of NO_x released at these altitudes is much greater than that of the nitrogen oxides found in the lower troposphere because, at aircraft cruising altitude, the lifetime of NO_x is relatively long (8 days), and the ozone formed at this altitude with the involvement of NO_x has a particularly strong radiative impact.

Volatile organic compounds (VOCs)

The VOCs (volatile organic compounds) found in the troposphere fall into various chemical categories (aliphatic and aromatic hydrocarbons, alcohols, aldehydes, ketones, fatty acids, etc.). Correspondingly, their ozone formation potentials vary widely. It makes sense, therefore, to distinguish between the following groups of substances, in accordance with their rates of reaction with OH radicals and ozone:

– inert VOCs with tropospheric lifetimes of more than one week (e.g. ethane, acetylene, propane, benzene, methanol, acetone);

- reactive VOCs with lifetimes of between half a day and one week (e. g. pentane, hexane, ethene, toluene, xylene, ethyl alcohol, methyl ethyl ketone);
- highly reactive VOCs with lifetimes of a few hours and less (propene and higher olefins, terpenes).

The concentrations and the temporal/spatial behaviour of the various organic compounds in the troposphere vary widely. Usually, VOC concentrations are much lower in the Southern Hemisphere than at northern middle and high latitudes. The rate at which VOC concentrations decrease with increasing altitude depends on the reactivity of the compound involved. Above the northern Atlantic Ocean, air traffic plays a role in the vertical distribution of VOCs. The concentrations of VOCs – most of which are man-made – are subject to more or less pronounced annual variations, with a broad minimum during the summer months. Biological sources of VOCs include vegetation and the biota in ocean surface water, mainly in the vicinity of coastlines. Isoprene and terpenes, which are produced almost exclusively by biological sources, are the most reactive tropospheric VOCs, and hence, they can be practically be measured only in the immediate vicinity of their sources (10).

Sulphur-based trace gases

Sulphurous trace gases are transformed into sulphuric acid by oxidation and subsequently lead to the formation of sulphate aerosol particles. They modify the Earth's radiation budget in various ways:

- directly by affecting incident solar radiation via their scattering and absorption capacity (see Section 2.2.2.1);
- indirectly by affecting the condensation processes that lead to cloud formation, thereby also affecting the scattering characteristics of clouds (see Section 2.2.2.1);
- indirectly by affecting (heterogeneous) chemical processes, in particular in the stratosphere (heterogeneous ozone depletion).

The most important sulphur-based trace gases in both the troposphere and the stratosphere include sulphur dioxide (SO_2), dimethyl sulphide (DMS), hydrogen sulphide (H_2S), and carbonyl sulphide (COS). These compounds are formed on the Earth's surface by various processes and released into the atmosphere. The most important man-made sources of these compounds are the combustion of fossil fuels and agricultural activities. In addition, sulphur-based compounds are also produced by natural microbial processes, and they are released by volcanic processes. Except for COS, the horizontal and vertical distribution of sulphur-based compounds in the troposphere varies widely.

The tropospheric lifetimes of DMS and H_2S are too short (rapid photochemical decomposition) for these compounds to reach the stratosphere. Surface emissions of SO_2 are also transformed into sulphate aerosol particles in the troposphere, which are then washed out by precipitation. COS is an exception because its lifetime is in the order of a few years, and it plays a major role in the formation of the "Junge layer" – a stratospheric aerosol layer found at an altitude of between 15 and 25 kilometers. Major volcanic eruptions such as that of El Chichón (1982) and that of the Pinatubo (1991) develop sufficient energy for larger amounts of SO_2 and H_2S to be transported into the stratosphere. At times of major volcanic activity, therefore, there is invariably a substantial increase in aerosol abundance in the „Junge layer". Lately, SO_2 emissions from the exhaust of high-flying aircraft have also been discussed as a source of these sulphate aerosols (30). Recent measurements have shown that background sulphate aerosol concentrations in the stratosphere increase by 5 percent annually during periods without major volcanic activity (31).

NO_2 seems to be quickly transformed into nitric acid on the surfaces of stratospheric aerosol particles which mainly consist of sulphuric acid and water in a ratio of 3 : 1 (25) (26). As a result, this NO_2 is no longer easily available for (temporarily) „neutralising" the ozone-depleting Cl and ClO radicals. This accelerates stratospheric ozone depletion, and thus, also affects the Earth's radiation budget.

2.2.1.5 Global warming potentials

The radiative activity of atmospheric greenhouse gases is referred to as the global warming potential (GWP) relative to CO_2 (in its current mean tropospheric mixing ratio). Based on the same number of molecules, the CH_4 molecule absorbs heat radiation about 21 times more effectively than the CO_2 molecule. The CFC-12 molecule is even about 15,800 times more effective than the CO_2 molecule. Based on these data, Table 2.1 provides an overview of the mean contributions of the most important radiatively active trace gases to the additional, man-made greenhouse effect during the Eighties. According to this table, CO_2 accounts for about 50 percent, CH_4 for 13 percent, N_2O for 5 percent, tropospheric ozone for 7 percent, and the two CFCs 11 and 12 account for 5 and 12 percent, respectively, of the man-made greenhouse effect. All the CFCs taken together account for 22 percent, while stratospheric water vapour accounts for 3 percent.

The GWPs listed in the table are only approximate estimates of the relative contributions of the various radiatively active trace gases to the additional, man-made greenhouse effect. For an accurate description of the actual conditions prevailing, it would be necessary to take into account temporal variations of the various trace gases' atmospheric mixing ratios (relative to CO_2), as well as differences in their spatial distribution and possible changes in their atmospheric lifetimes (due to, for instance, changes in chemical processes). Of course, this also applies to CO_2 which is used as a scaling factor for calculating GWPs. For this reason, the GWPs will have to be continuously revised.

Despite these problems, CO_2 can be expected to continue to be the predominant cause of the additional, man-made greenhouse effect, because of its high emission rates and its relatively long atmospheric lifetime.

2.2.2 Other factors affecting the climate

In addition to the directly and indirectly acting atmospheric trace gases discussed in Chapter 2.2.1 above, the following chapter provides up-to-date information on some other parameters such as aerosol particles, clouds, surface albedo and solar irradiation. These parameters also affect the Earth's radiation budget by modifying not only long-wave terrestrial heat radiation but also the solar radiation flux absorbed by the Earth. So far, it has been possible to assess these effects at best in terms of the direction and the order of magnitude of their impact. However, current findings suggest that it is very likely that the additional, man-made greenhouse effect will play the predominant role in the next 100 or 200 years, if all climate parameters are taken into account.

2.2.2.1 Aerosol particles

Air-borne solid and liquid particles with diameters between 0.001 and 100 μm are referred to as aerosol particles. (Cloud, fog and rainfall droplets, by definition, are no aerosol particles.) Major natural sources of aerosol particles include wind erosion – in particular in desert regions (dust storms) – and the so-called "sea spray" above the oceans. In addition, various human activities also lead to aerosol particle emissions, either directly or indirectly via the emission of gases which are converted into (larger) particles in the atmosphere (gas-to-particle conversion). Man-made emissions of aerosol particles have mainly been observed in industrial agglomerations.

Because of their short tropospheric lifetimes – which range between a few days and several weeks, depending on their injection altitude and washout by precipitation – and because of the uneven distribution of their sources, the global distribution of tropospheric aerosol particles varies widely, in terms of both time and space. No reliable statements can be made about temporal trends. However, substantial increases in aerosol particle concentrations have been observed in some industrialised regions. Visibility measurements, for instance, which have been carried out in eastern part of North America since 1948, have shown that haziness has increased during the summer months (32). In other industrialised regions, however, aerosol concentrations in surface air layers have tended to decline, or there has at least been no clear-cut trend.

The greatest impact that tropospheric aerosol particles have on the climate is probably their effect on cloud formation, as well as the optical properties of clouds and precipitation. While surface air layers usually contain sufficient concentrations of condensation nuclei (on average, between 500 and 1,000 particles per cubic centimeter above the oceans, and between 10,000 and 15,000 particles per cubic centimeter above the continents), there are only about 100 particles per cubic meter in the middle and upper troposphere. Consequently, a general change in particle concentrations above the oceans and in the middle troposphere will have a particularly strong impact on cloud formation. In air masses with low concentrations of condensation nuclei, any increase in aerosol particle concentrations will lead not only to more extensive cloud formation but often also to shifts in the droplet size spectrum towards smaller droplet diameters, which increases the clouds' reflectivity (albedo) (33). However, it is only in a few regions of the Northern Hemisphere, if at all, that this effect can compensate for the man-made greenhouse effect due to the increase in tropospheric trace gas mixing ratios. In addition, it is doubtful what the overall response of clouds will be – in terms of cloud amounts and types – to the new dynamic conditions brought about by climate change.

In the stratosphere, the distribution of aerosol particle concentrations is relatively homogeneous. It is controlled by quasi-continuous natural and man-made emissions of precursor gases (mainly COS and SO_2) from the Earth's surface, as well as (increasingly) by aircraft exhaust emissions and major volcanic eruptions. The mean stratospheric lifetime of aerosol particles amounts to a few years. Measurements of the so-called background concentrations have shown that, at times of low volcanic activity, the aerosol particle concentration increases at a rate of 5 percent per year (31). Should this trend persist, in a few decades' time the stratospheric background concentration of aerosols will be as high as after major volcanic eruptions.

According to satellite data (NIMBUS 7), the eruption of the Pinatubo in the Philippines in June 1991 injected about 20 million tonnes of SO_2 directly into the stratosphere – 50 percent more than the SO_2 emissions caused by the eruption of El Chichón in 1982 (1).

It has been demonstrated that aerosol particle emissions from major volcanic eruptions have an impact on the Earth's radiation budget. Due to the small sizes of these particles (mean diameter of about 0.5 μm) and due to their chemical composition (mainly sulphuric acid droplets), they mainly have a scattering effect on solar light, while they absorb very little long-wave radiation. So the overall effect that major volcanic eruptions have is that surface temperatures decrease. The latest model predictions with regard to the effect of the Pinatubo eruption (which, however, did not take into account a potential buffering effect by the oceans) suggest that temperatures in the Northern Hemisphere will decrease by between 0.3 and 0.5 °C over the next two years (34).

2.2.2.2 Clouds

The impact of clouds and the associated feedback effects on the radiation budget and the climate are highly complex. On the one hand, cloud surfaces – because of their higher albedo – reflect more incident solar energy than most land surfaces, thereby reducing the greenhouse effect in cloud-covered regions. On the other hand, high-altitude clouds release less long-wave radiation, thereby increasing the greenhouse effect. In terms of their impact on the climate, therefore, clouds have two countervailing effects. High clouds – in particular cirrus clouds (thin ice clouds found in the upper troposphere and the lower stratosphere) – predominantly exacerbate the greenhouse effect. An expansion of cirrus clouds over larger areas will therefore lead to warming. It is very likely that aircraft emissions (water vapour and particles) play an important role in this context (35). Low clouds, on the other hand, tend to lead to lower temperatures.

In order to be able to assess the global impact of clouds on the radiation budget, it is very important to have information about the frequency, as well as the global and regional distribution, of the various cloud types. Analyses of satellite data have shown that the albedo effect of clouds predominates, and hence, that they tend to attenuate the greenhouse effect (36). This applies in particular to the mid-latitudes of both hemispheres, while the clouds' albedo effect and greenhouse effect almost cancel each other out at tropical latitudes. This suggests that the Earth's clouds – in their current form and distribution – increase the mean meridional energy balance gradient. In this context, it should be pointed out that clouds also modify the vertical energy distribution in the climate system. In the solar spectral region, for instance, they have a very strong impact on the amount of solar radiation reaching the Earth's surface. Any changes in cloud conditions can therefore lead to changes in warming, in particular of the oceans. The atmosphere is the main beneficiary of the energy gained by the reduction of long-wave radiation.

It is not yet possible to predict the response of the clouds to the progressive warming of the Earth's surface, i. e. the regional and global changes in the frequency and distribution of specific cloud types. The difficulties involved in such predictions are compounded by the fact that they have to take into consideration not only the increase in tropospheric water vapour concentrations but also other man-made parameters such as an increasing input of aerosol particles (condensation nuclei) and possibly an increase in the formation of cirrus clouds.

2.2.2.3 Surface albedo

The Earth's surface albedo is rising as a result of desertification, increasing salinity of arid soils, large-scale deforestation (in the tropics, Canada and Siberia), urbanisation and the use of intensive farming methods. All these changes taken together are estimated to have caused an increase in surface albedo by 0.6 percent over the past 1,000 years, and by 0.1 percent over the past 20 years alone (37).

While the resulting impact on the Earth's radiation budget is relatively low, this change in surface albedo strongly affects the energy balance of the Earth's surface as such. Changes in surface characteristics, for instance, produce significant changes with regard to both the water balance and soil roughness. However, it is not yet possible to make reliable assessments of the net effects of these changes on surface energy fluxes.

2.2.2.4 Insolation

The sun is the main source of energy for physical, chemical and biological processes which occur on the Earth's surface, and it is the "driving force" for physical and chemical processes in the atmosphere. Any changes in energy irradiation can understandably have a major impact on the climate. Solar radiation is subject to temporal variations of various time scales. Short-term variations within a period of a few days, caused by physical processes in the solar photosphere, apparently have no effect on the climate. Studies which were conducted to assess the impact of the eleven-year solar cycle on the Earth's climate have shown that, at the upper boundary of the atmosphere, insolation increases as the number of (dark) sun spots increases (38). Between 1980 and 1986, for instance, mean insolation decreased – in keeping with the solar cycle – by 0.2 watts per square meter, and after this period it increased again. However, a major

Table 2.4: *Current Global Contributions of Various Emission Sources Towards the Man-Made Greenhouse Effect*[1]
(CO$_2$=carbon dioxide; CH$_4$=methane; NO$_x$=nitrogen oxides; CO=carbon monoxide; NMVOCs=non-methane
volatile organic compounds; CFCs=chlorofluorocarbons; N$_2$O=nitrous oxide=laughing gas)

Emission sources	Shares (rounded)	Breakdown into trace gases (rounded)	Causes
Energy incl. transport	50%	40% CO$_2$ 10% CH$_4$ and O$_3$ (O$_3$ is formed by its precursors NO$_x$, CO and NMVOCs)	Trace gas emissions due to the use of fossil fuels (i.e. coal, oil and gas), both in the conversion sector (esp. electricity generation, district heating, and refineries) and in the end-point energy sectors, i.e. households, small-scale users (crafts, services, public institutions, etc.), industry and transport
Chemical products (CFCs, halons, etc.)[2]	20%	20% CFCs, halons, etc.	Emissions of CFCs, halons, etc.
Tropical deforestation	15%	10% CO$_2$ 5% other trace gases, in particular N$_2$O, CH$_4$ and CO	Emissions due to burning and decomposition of tropical forests, including increasing soil emissions
Agriculture and other emission sources (landfills, etc.)	15%	15%, mainly CH$_4$, N$_2$O and CO$_2$	Emissions due to: — anaerobic conversion processes (CH$_4$ release from cattle farming, rice paddies, etc.), — fertilisation (N$_2$O), — landfills (CH$_4$), — cement factories (CO$_2$), — etc.

impact of the eleven-year cycle on the global climate can be precluded for two reasons: first of all, the radiation flux changes involved are very small – for reference: mean solar radiation flux density amounts to 1,368 ±10 watts per square meter (solar constant); and secondly, the sign changes in relatively short intervals (cf. Chapter 4).

Another parameter which may affect solar radiation is the sun's diameter and its temporal variation. The cycle of its variation extends over a period of about 80 years (39). It has also been suggested that there may be a relationship between minimum levels of sunspot activity and changes in solar radiation intensity. The impact of variations in these two solar parameters on mean global surface temperatures has been estimated at a maximum of 0.2 °C (1).

The theory developed by Milankovic (40) to explain the appearance of glacial periods shows that even relatively minor changes in various orbital parameters – and hence, in insolation energy – can lead to rather dramatic climate change, if they occur over long periods of time (between 10,000 and 100,000 years) and if their primary effects are adequately enhanced in the Earth's climate system (40).

2.3 Causes and Sources

Worldwide, the use of the fossil fuels coal, oil and gas for energy purposes accounts for about 50 percent of the additional, man-made greenhouse effect. In addition, various products of the chemical industry, tropical deforestation, as well as agriculture and other sectors – in descending order – also exacerbate the greenhouse effect (cf. Table 2.4).

◀ Notes to Table 2.4:

1) These rounded figures have already been quoted by the Enquete Commission in the past few months. Considering the broad range of contributions of the various trace gases towards the man-made greenhouse effect and the wide range of uncertainty involved in attributing trace gas emissions to the various sources, only rough, approximate figures can currently be provided. Within the range of current uncertainties and trace gas contributions, the figures quoted above concur with those specified by the IPCC in its final report published in summer 1990.

The IPCC report specifies the following contributions and ranges for the various emission sources:
— energy: 46 percent (38—54 percent),
— chemical products (CFCs, halons, etc.): 24 percent (no range specified, although the absorption coefficients are uncertain in relation to those of CO_2, CH_4 and N_2O),
— deforestation: 18 percent (9-26 percent),
— agriculture: 9 percent (4-13 percent),
— other emission sources (landfills, cement factories, etc.): 3 percent (range: 1-4 percent).

2) CFCs, halons and other compounds which both add to stratospheric ozone depletion and exacerbate the man-made greenhouse effect

2.3.1 Energy including transport

2.3.1.1 The global energy situation

Since energy-related CO_2 emissions account for 80 percent of the energy sector's overall greenhouse effect, this chapter first of all concentrates on the sources of CO_2 emissions.

Before coal was introduced as the first fossil fuel available during the second half of the seventeenth century, man's supply of energy was mainly based on extensive use of renewable energy sources, in particular wood, hydropower and wind (41). The importance of oil began to grow in the late nineteenth century, and two decades later, man began to make intensive use of natural gas (42). The increasing use of fossil fuels has been accompanied ever since by exponential increases in carbon dioxide emissions. This development was interrupted only by the two World Wars, the international economic crisis in 1929 and the energy price hikes in the wake of the two oil price crises in 1973 and 1979 (cf. Fig. 2.8). In the past two decades, global energy consumption has increased by an average of about 2 percent annually (10). However, preliminary estimates for 1990 and 1991 suggest that global energy-related CO_2 emissions – including the emisssions from the oil well fires in Kuwait (amounting to about one percent of global energy-related CO_2 emissions) – have stagnated or even declined (43).

This development over the past two years, which is desirable from the perspective of climate protection policy, however, has not been the result of global or national CO_2 reduction strategies; instead, it has been mainly due to the fundamental political and economic changes in the Eastern European countries and in the Commonwealth of Independent States (CIS), and to the recession in the United States, the country with the highest CO_2 emissions worldwide.

In 1989, global energy-related CO_2 emissions amounted to 21.6 billion tonnes. The industrialised nations were responsible for three-quarters of these emissions, with the OECD countries accounting for 47 percent (or 10 billion tonnes of CO_2) and the industrialised, former centrally planned economies accounting for 25 percent of total emissions (cf. Fig. 2.9).

Today's industrialised nations have been the sources of as much as over 90 percent of the CO_2 emissions which have accumulated over a period of about 100 years and which have caused the increase in the atmospheric CO_2 concentration to its current level. This underlines the industrialised nations' responsibility when it comes to initiating measures designed to mitigate the man-made greenhouse effect.

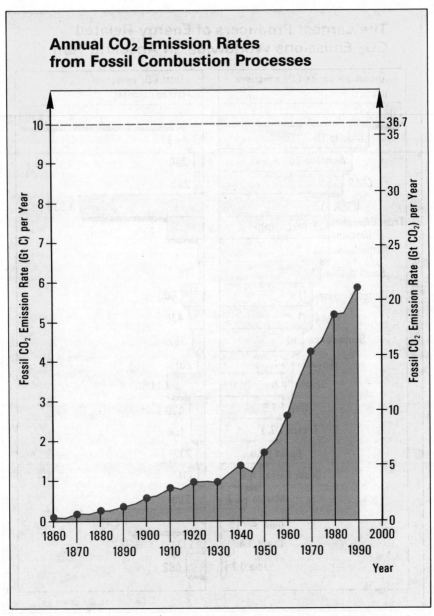

Fig. 2.8: Annual global CO$_2$ emission rates from fossil combustion processes since 1860 (in Gt of carbon per year, and in Gt of CO$_2$ per year), from (1)

1 tonne of carbon (C) corresponds to 3.67 tonnes of CO$_2$.

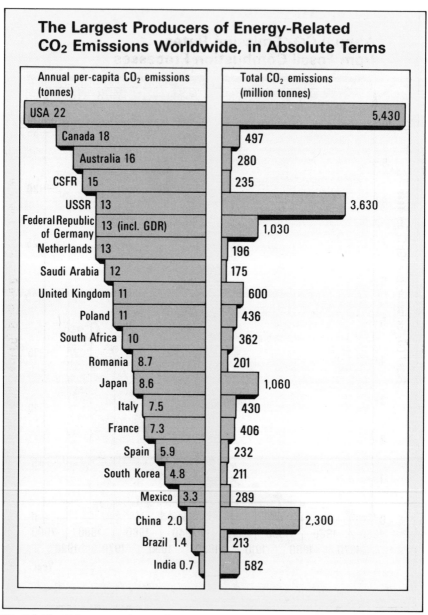

The Largest Producers of Energy-Related CO_2 Emissions Worldwide, in Absolute Terms

Annual per-capita CO_2 emissions (tonnes)	Total CO_2 emissions (million tonnes)
USA 22	5,430
Canada 18	497
Australia 16	280
CSFR 15	235
USSR 13	3,630
Federal Republic of Germany 13 (incl. GDR)	1,030
Netherlands 13	196
Saudi Arabia 12	175
United Kingdom 11	600
Poland 11	436
South Africa 10	362
Romania 8.7	201
Japan 8.6	1,060
Italy 7.5	430
France 7.3	406
Spain 5.9	232
South Korea 4.8	211
Mexico 3.3	289
China 2.0	2,300
Brazil 1.4	213
India 0.7	582

Fig. 2.9: The 21 largest producers of energy-related CO_2 emissions worldwide (1989) (44)

Because of differences in definitions and emission factors, CO_2 emission data from various literature sources may deviate from each other.

60

National per-capita CO_2 emissions vary by a factor of up to 20 (cf. Fig. 2.10). The data shown in Fig. 2.10 illustrate that future reductions of CO_2 emissions will have to be achieved primarily by the industrialised nations because most developing countries feel that it is necessary for them to increase their use of cheap and widely available energy sources (i.e. in general fossil fuels). However, current forecasts of global energy consumption are still based on the assumption that energy consumption will increase in all countries. The IEA, for instance, expects world energy consumption to increase by 40 percent by the year 2005, with half of this increase being attributed to the developing countries and the other half being shared in roughly equal parts between the OECD countries and the Central and Eastern European countries including the former Soviet Union (45). At the last World Energy Conference, which was held in Montreal in 1989, global CO_2 emissions were expected to rise by as much as 45-70 percent by the year 2020 (46).

Against the background of the changing conditions in the former centrally planned economies in Eastern Europe and Asia, and bearing in mind the financial limitations which many developing countries are subject to when it comes to importing energy sources, it would make sense to review such forecasts – which are extrapolations of past trends – in order to determine whether they can be upheld after the changes that have occurred in the geopolitical environment.

2.3.1.2 *The national energy situation*

In 1990, energy-related carbon dioxide emissions of the Federal Republic of Gemany and the GDR totalled about one billion tonnes of CO_2 (i.e. 13 tonnes of CO_2 per capita), thereby accounting for 32 percent of total EC emissions (including the GDR) (48). In the Federal Republic of Germany, CO_2 emissions had reached a peak in the late Seventies and then gradually edged downwards in the following decade. This was mainly due to improvements in energy efficiency induced by energy price increases in 1979, and to the increasing use of gas and nuclear energy. Since the fall of the Berlin Wall on 9 November 1989, the CO_2 emissions of the Federal Republic of Germany (including both the old and the new federal states) have declined more rapidly than before. This has been due to the fact that, after the collapse of the centrally planned economy in the former GDR and after domestic migration movements, the country's overall economic performance has increased because of the use of modern technologies which have helped to improve process efficiency.

The sources of energy-related CO_2 emissions can be subdivided into the power station sector (as the largest energy consumer in the field of energy

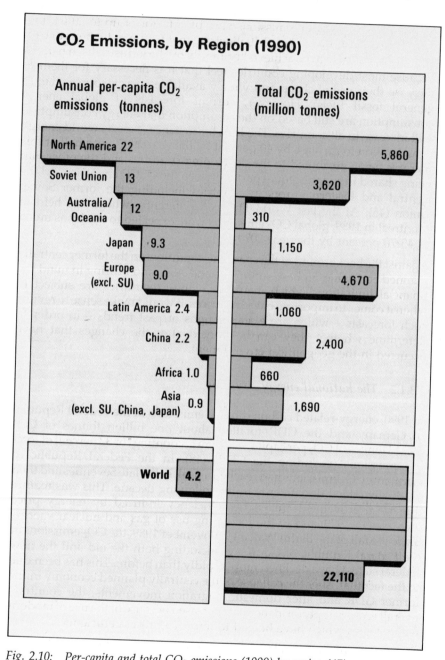

Fig. 2.10: *Per-capita and total CO₂ emissions (1990) by region (47)*

conversion) and the following energy consumption sectors (cf. left-hand columns in Fig. 2.11):

- industry (including other consumers in the field of energy conversion, e.g. refineries and coking plants),
- private households,
- small-scale energy users (e.g. public buildings, craft establishments, agriculture), and
- transport.

If one concentrates on the emissions directly related with a given energy use, power stations and district heating plants were the largest single source of such emissions in 1990 (37 percent); the other energy consumption sectors accounted for roughly equal shares of these direct CO_2 emissions (20 percent each).

In this analysis, however, energy consumers are only attributed the CO_2 emissions directly caused by them. This means that CO_2 emissions associated with the use of energy – e.g. electricity generation – are not ascribed to the electricity consumer but to the conversion sector involved. In other words, no CO_2 emissions are debited to the final consumers for their electricity demand. In order to describe the true situation with regard to emissions caused by energy sources used by final consumers, one has to add the CO_2 emissions caused during production and conversion. The corresponding distribution of energy-related CO_2 emissions is illustrated by the right-hand columns in Fig. 2.11.

In this figure, energy-related CO_2 emissions are broken down into the various consumption sectors. In addition to this sectoral presentation based on energy demand, it is also quite common to adopt an energy supply perspective and to break down CO_2 emissions by energy source. This breakdown is provided by Fig. 2.12 for the period between 1970 and 1991.

In view of the increasingly manifest global climate change, and taking into consideration the level of radiatively active trace gas emissions released by the Federal Republic of Germany, the Enquete Commission on "Preventive Measures to Protect the Earth's Atmosphere" – which had been established by the German Bundestag during the eleventh legislative period – recommended that, relative to 1987 levels, energy-related CO_2 emissions should be reduced by 30 percent by the year 2005, by another 20 percent by the year 2020, and by another 30 percent by the year 2050 (10). In order to achieve the emission reduction target defined for the year 2005, the Commission developed three scenarios: "Energy Policy", "Nuclear Energy Phase-Out", and "Increasing Nuclear Energy Use".

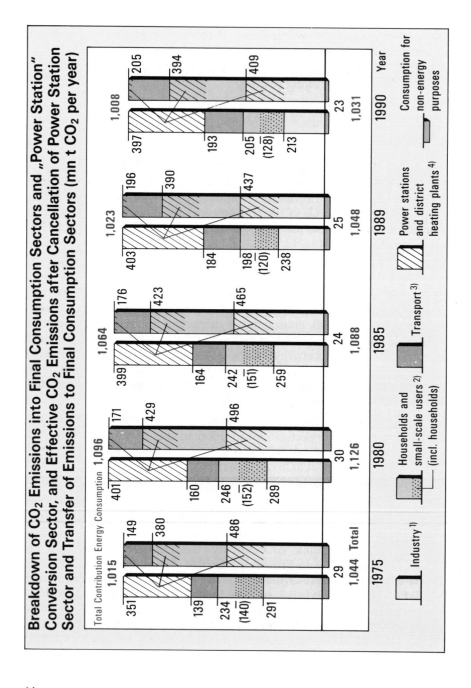

Breakdown of CO_2 Emissions into Final Consumption Sectors and „Power Station" Conversion Sector, and Effective CO_2 Emissions after Cancellation of Power Station Sector and Transfer of Emissions to Final Consumption Sectors (mn t CO_2 per year)

What these three scenarios – all of which permitted attainment of the emission reduction target defined by technical and economic criteria – had in common was that they attached top priority to increasing energy efficiency and energy conservation (10) (cf. Fig. 2.13).

Since the presentation of these recommendations, there have been changes in several important general conditions which make it difficult for the old federal states of the Federal Republic of Germany to attain the emission reduction target by the year 2005:

- The investments required to achieve increases in energy efficiency have to compete with the additional investment needs that have arisen after German unification with regard to restructuring the economic framework in the new federal states.

- The fundamental social and economic changes that have occurred in the Eastern European countries and in the former Soviet Union have had the same effects.

- The room for isolated national action is being curtailed by the emerging single European market within the EC, and in particular, by the introduction of a common European electricity market which is currently being discussed.

Against the background of these circumstances, the Interministerial Task Force on "CO_2 Reductions" (IMA), which had been established by the German Federal Government, assumes that it will be possible to reduce CO_2 emissions for the Federal Republic of Germany as a whole by 12 percent by the year 2010, if the various regulatory and fiscal measures recommended by the IMA and adopted by the German Federal Government are in fact implemented without any other energy policy interven-

---

◀ Fig. 2.11: Breakdown of CO_2 emissions into final consumption sectors and the power-station conversion sector, and effective CO_2 emissions after cancellation of the power station sector and transfer of emissions to the final consumption sectors (million tonnes) (49)

1) Other conversion sector facilities, manufacturing sector and other mining sector operations; industrial power stations: heat generation only.
2) Including military agencies.
3) Road transport including agriculture, forestry and building industry transport; military, rail, water, and air transport; including marine and air transport originating from the former territory of the Federal Republic of Germany, in accordance with the fuel volumes specified in the energy budget.
4) In the case of industrial power stations, electricity generation only.
*) Provisional data.
Differences between the data shown above and the data specified in Figures 2.9 and 2.12 are due to differences in computation methodology, data sources and emission factors.

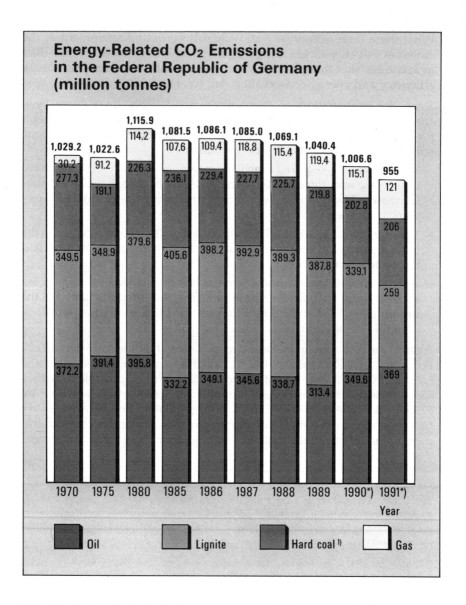

Energy-Related CO₂ Emissions in the Federal Republic of Germany (million tonnes)

	1970	1975	1980	1985	1986	1987	1988	1989	1990*)	1991*)
Total	1,029.2	1,022.6	1,115.9	1,081.5	1,086.1	1,085.0	1,069.1	1,040.4	1,006.6	955
Gas	30.2	91.2	114.2	107.6	109.4	118.8	115.4	119.4	115.1	121
Hard coal ¹⁾	277.3	191.1	226.3	236.1	229.4	227.7	225.7	219.8	202.8	206
Lignite	349.5	348.9	379.6	405.6	398.2	392.9	389.3	387.8	339.1	259
Oil	372.2	391.4	395.8	332.2	349.1	345.6	338.7	313.4	349.6	369

Oil   Lignite   Hard coal ¹⁾   Gas

N.B.: Calculated on the basis of primary energy consumption less consumption for non-energy purposes. Emission factors from Jülich Research Centre. Minor discrepancies with the data in Figures 2.9 and 2.11 are due to differences in computation methodology and emission factors.
*) Provisional data;   ¹) Including solid fuels.

Source: Federal Ministry of Economics, III D 3; 1991 data: calculated by the Enquete Commission based on Schiffer, 1992.

tions (51). The latest energy forecast for the Federal Republic of Germany, commissioned by the Federal Ministry of Economics, has come to similar conclusions: CO_2 emissions are expected to decline from 1,076 million tonnes in 1987 to 964 million tonnes by the year 2005 (i.e. by slightly more than 10 percent) (52). Hence, in order to achieve the reduction targets defined in the Cabinet's decision of 7 November 1990 (reduction of CO_2 emissions by 25 percent in the old federal states and a more drastic reduction in the new federal states) and in the Cabinet's decision of 11 December 1991 (reduction of CO_2 emissions by between 25 and 30 percent in the old and the new federal states taken together), there is a need for further action, as already outlined by the Enquete Commission on "Preventive Measures to Protect the Earth's Atmosphere" during the eleventh legislative period.

2.3.1.3 Transport

Because of increasingly close international economic relations, there is a growing need for transport of persons and goods. Worldwide, transport accounts for 27 percent of total energy consumption. In the Federal Republic of Germany, the transport sector's share of total energy demand has increased in the past 30 years from about 15 percent to over 25 percent, which has led to the following breakdown of end-point energy consumption by sector (Federal Republic of Germany, 1990):

Industry	30.4 percent
Transport	28.2 percent
Households	25.0 percent
Small-scale users	16.4 percent

Environmental pollution caused by the transport sector is rising, not only in absolute terms but also in relative terms as compared to other energy consumption sectors. This is mainly due to private motor vehicle transport and the changes it generates.

Emission reductions achieved in the past 15 years by improvements in engine and motor vehicle technology have not been able to offset the increase in emissions caused by growing traffic volumes. This increase in traffic has been due to increasingly interlinked economic structures (e. g. locations of production sites and sales markets, relative positions of

◀ *Fig. 2.12: Energy-related CO_2 emissions in the Federal Republic of Germany (including the GDR), by source of energy, for selected years, 1970-1991 (million tonnes) (50)*

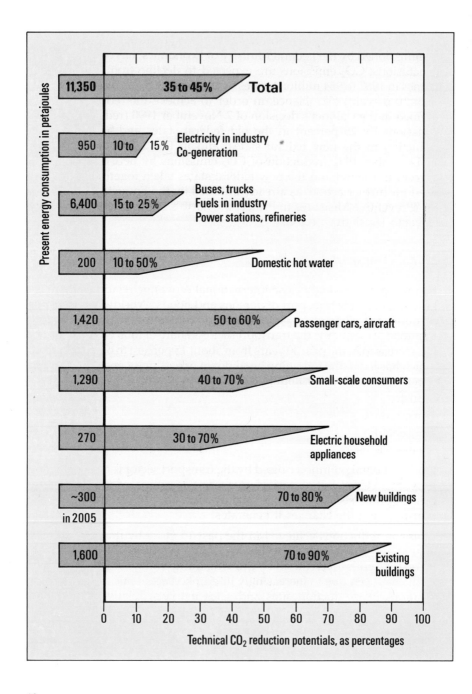

homes and workplaces, locations of recreational facilities, etc.), energy losses caused by high traffic density and congestion, and additional energy consumption as a result of higher expectations in terms of motor vehicle quality (more powerful engines, more comfort, higher top speeds). Increases in energy consumption due to increasingly close ties between different locations are a consequence, in particular, of the Single European Market of the European Community and of the integration of Eastern Europe.

Within the European Community, the motor freight industry has been expanding for many years and is now one of the most important ground transport modes. In fact, road haulage alone accounts for half of Europe's total goods transport volume. Between 1984 and 1989, road haulage in the Community increased by 50.1 percent at national level and by 84.4 percent at international level. In the same period of time, rail transport grew by only 7.3 percent at national level and by 12.8 percent at international level.

Annual growth rates of air transport in Europe can be expected to continue to range above 6 percent in the next few years. The spectacular growth rates observed in passenger and air freight volumes in the past demonstrate that the European air transport market is in a process of fundamental change. In the past 10 years, air passenger volumes within the Community and with third countries have increased by 65.6 percent, and air freight volumes have risen by as much as 105.5 percent (54).

The emissions caused by the energy sector comprise all the radiatively active trace gases, with carbon dioxide emissions accounting for the largest percentage contribution to the greenhouse effect.

Carbon dioxide (CO_2)

About 20 percent of global carbon emissions are caused by the combustion of fossil fuels in the transport sector. Figure 2.14 provides an international percentage breakdown of transport-related carbon dioxide emissions by country. This shows that the industrialised nations account for two-thirds of global CO_2 emissions in the transport sector, while all the developing countries taken together account for less than one-fifth. The country with the highest emissions worldwide is the United States which accounts for one-third of global CO_2 production (55).

◀ *Fig. 2.13: Technical potentials achievable by increasing energy efficiency in the Federal Republic of Germany, excluding the former GDR (percentages, relative to the energy consumption volume in the respective field of application in 1987) (10)*

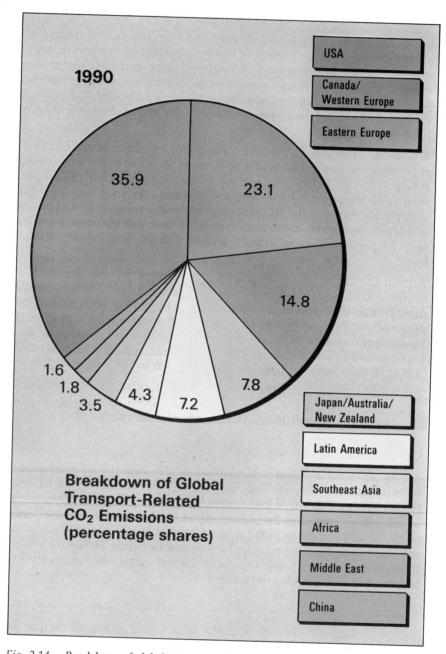

Fig. 2.14:   *Breakdown of global transport-related CO₂ emissions (55)*

Water vapour (H₂O)

Water vapour (H$_2$O)

Stratospheric water vapour emissions caused by air traffic affect the Earth's climate by adding to the man-made greenhouse effect. Aircraft fuel is mainly composed of hydrocarbons which form carbon dioxide and water vapour when they are burnt in the aircraft engines together with atmospheric oxygen. Compared with evaporation on the Earth's surface, the water vapour emission volumes are very small. However, in conjunction with the water vapour produced by methane oxidation, it makes a major contribution towards increasing stratospheric water vapour concentrations, which are low under normal conditions (cf. Chapter 2.2.1.2). Commercial aircraft cruising at the level of the tropopause form contrails which consist of ice particles. If there is sufficient ambient humidity, these ice particles can lead to an increase in the amount of clouds. The sunlight continues to reach the Earth's surface unhindered irrespective of whether there are thin ice clouds. However, terrestrial heat radiation is substantially reduced by the presence of such thin clouds, leading to an increase in surface temperatures.

Nitrogen oxides (NO$_x$)

The combustion of fossil fuels accounts for about two-thirds (20 mn t) of global nitrogen oxide emissions. While considerable progress has been achieved in the past few years with regard to reducing carbon monoxide and hydrocarbon emissions, the increasing number of motor vehicles and higher mileages have led to an increase in NO_x emissions despite the installation of catalytic converters. This increase in emissions has more than offset the reductions achieved with regard to emissions from power stations and industry.

When exposed to intensive solar radiation, nitrogen oxides (NO_x) and volatile organic compounds (VOCs) form tropospheric ozone (O_3), which accounts for 7 percent of the man-made greenhouse effect. In the Federal Republic of Germany, about 80 percent of the pollutants which produce tropospheric ozone in summer are due to emissions from the transport sector. In addition, the larger number of ozone alarms set off by the responsible authorities during the summer months directly affects human activities (e. g.. limited access to outdoor areas for children and elderly people, having to refrain from physically strenuous activities, etc.).

Sulphur dioxide (SO$_2$)

Kerosine, which is used as aircraft fuel, contains sulphur which is released in the form of sulphur dioxide by combustion. The impact of these emissions depends not only on the amounts released but also on the altitude at which these emissions occur.

At aircraft cruising altitudes, the impact of sulphur dioxide emissions is much greater than on the Earth's surface because of:

– longer lifetimes,
– lower background concentrations,
– higher radiative activity.

In the particularly sensitive polar regions, aeroplanes cruise at altitudes at which ozone is depleted. The SO_2 volumes released by them are large enough in order to lead to a substantial increase in sulphate aerosol concentrations in the lower stratosphere, thereby contributing towards ozone depletion.

Nitrous oxide (N_2O) and chlorofluorocarbons (CFCs)

Emissions of nitrous oxide (N_2O) and CFCs from the transport sector should not be neglected. About 68 percent of the CFC-based refrigerants produced worldwide is used for automotive air-conditioning systems; this corresponds to 75,000 tonnes of CFCs annually. Another 120,000 tonnes of CFCs are used for the production of automotive parts. Motor vehicles equipped with catalytic converters have N_2O emissions which are ten times higher than they otherwise would be; hence, such motor vehicles are not a negligible source of nitrous oxide emissions (56).

2.3.2 Deforestation

According to the FAO definition, the term "forest" denotes a plant community mainly consisting of trees which, at maturity, reach a height of at least 7 meters and shade at least 10 percent of the ground (10).

The Earth's forests – like the oceans – are among the most important ecosystems for humanity's survival. They play an extremely significant role in the atmospheric cycles of substances such as carbon, nitrogen and oxygen, and thus have a key impact on the chemical composition of the atmosphere. Forests help to regulate the climate, and they are involved in the water balance and in the hydrological cycle. They protect soils from erosion, promote soil formation at temperate and northern latitudes, are a source of food and offer human beings a variety of economic and social benefits.

Although forests cover only about 25 percent of the Earth's land surface, they give shelter to more animal and plant species – and contribute more towards the development of new species – than any other ecosystem. It is particularly important to preserve this diversity of species.

In 1980, the total surface area covered by forests and shrubs worldwide amounted to 53 million square kilometers, which can be broken down into the following regions (62):

Soviet Union	9.30 million sq. km
Europe	1.78 million sq. km
Asia	6.69 million sq. km
South America	11.25 million sq. km
Africa	13.39 million sq. km
North and Central America	9.01 million sq. km
Pacific Islands	1.58 million sq. km
Total	53.00 million sq. km

The following table shows the surface area covered by the three major forest ecotypes (63):

Tropical forests		19.0 million sq. km
of which: Wet forests	10.0 million sq. km	
Dry forests	9.0 million sq. km	
Boreal forests		9.2 million sq. km
Temperate forests		7.7 million sq. km
Total		35.9 million sq. km

Non-tropical forests

Forests at temperate latitudes and boreal forests currently act as a CO_2 sink since – due to human interventions – they fail to reach their maximum growth, and hence, accumulate biomass. In addition, forest areas in ECE countries have grown by about 2.5 percent since the late nineteenth century. Forests at temperate latitudes currently store a total of 25 Gt of carbon, roughly half of which is stored in living biomass. Boreal forests store a total of 190 Gt of carbon, one-third of which is stored in living biomass (63).

At mid-latitudes, forest growth rates might be adversely affected by the increasing percentages of damaged trees in Central Europe and in North

America. However, FAO surveys suggest that the forest stock per surface unit has grown and that annual growth rates of forests in European countries have increased. According to the FAO findings, forest stocks grew by an average of about 12 percent between 1970 and 1980, and annual growth rates went up by an average of about 9 percent. FAO believes that this may be explained by, among other things, higher plant density in managed forests. In the non-European industrialised nations, there is no evidence of a similar development. Overall, FAO expects the biomass of European forests to increase by 190 million cubic meters annually, which would correspond to a storage of 60 million tonnes of carbon (cf. Table 2.5).

In this context, it should be pointed out that the data used are of relatively poor quality. Consistent surveys of the biomass per surface unit are available for very few countries only. In the Federal Republic of Germany, for instance, the amount of biomass identified increased by 90 percent after a new surveying method was introduced in 1983.

It is still not possible to assess the magnitude of CO_2 emissions caused by suspected deforestation in Canada and Sibiria involving an estimated surface area of between 1 and 3 million ha. Nor is it possible to quantify the CO_2 emissions caused by the thinning of the crowns of damaged trees and by increased decomposition of humus in forest soils.

Non-tropical forests currently seem to have a minor impact on global climate change. However, it should be borne in mind that future global warming will considerably accelerate the decomposition rates of dead organic matter. This might lead to the release of an additional volume of up to 200 Gt of carbon in the next few decades, which would exacerbate the greenhouse effect.

Tropical forests

According to the FAO's 1990 Forest Resources Assessment Project, tropical forests covered a total surface area of 18.82 million square kilometers (as compared to 19.35 mn sq. km in 1980), and the annual deforestation rate amounted to 169,000 square kilometers (113,000 sq. km in 1980). In other words, the annual deforestation rate increased from 0.6 percent in 1980 to 0.9 percent in 1990, or by about 50 percent. This rate varied widely from country to country.

According to Myers (60), wet tropical forests covered a surface area of 8 million square kilometers in 1989, and the deforestation rate for the same year amounted to 142,000 square kilometers. To Myers, this suggested that, between 1979 and 1989, the annual deforestation rate increased to 1.8 percent, or by 90 percent. Shifting agriculture – i.e. people migrating to

Table 2.5: Tree Biomass of Closed Forests in ECE Countries
(million tonnes dry solids) (FAO, 1985)

	Exploitable closed forests						
	Total tree biomass	Stumps and roots	Above-ground tree biomass				
			Total	Inventoried material			Other above ground
				Total	Wood	Bark	
Albania	45	8	57	40	37	4	17
Austria	504	83	421	362	328	34	59
Belgium	62	7	55	37	33	4	10
Bulgaria	218	35	183	130	104	26	53
Cyprus	2	—	2	1	1	—	—
Czechoslovakia	583	104	479	390	357	33	89
Denmark	40	4	36	21	19	2	14
Federal Republic of Germany	710	91	618	459	408	51	159
Finland	1,010	148	862	643	545	98	219
France	1,165	77	1,091	840	798	72	251
German Democratic Republic	286	37	249	186	165	21	63
Greece	107	28	79	64	57	7	16
Hungary	168	25	143	143	118	25	—
Iceland	—	—	—	—	—	—	—
Ireland	19	3	16	13	11	2	3
Israel	2	—	2	1	1	—	—
Italy	299	145	355	203	255	28	72
Luxembourg	10	1	9	7	6	1	3
Netherlands	15	2	13	10	9	1	3
Norway	294	43	251	201	173	28	50
Poland	826	55	771	570	492	78	201
Portugal	139	17	122	100	87	13	21
Romania	942	117	826	590	538	59	23
Spain	388	78	309	185	171	14	125
Sweden	1,446	233	1,213	959	844	115	251
Switzerland	211	27	184	136	121	15	48
Turkey	416	12	404	334	205	49	70
United Kingdom	143	18	124	93	80	12	32
Yugoslavia	707	84	625	566	532	34	59
Europa	10,952	1,482	9,499	7,371	6,575	796	2,127
USSR	41,070	6,290	34,780	28,206	26,280	1,915	6,574
Canada	13,799	1,156	12,612	8,872	7,803	1,069	3,770
United States	16,931	1,893	15,038	17,014	1,021	1,802	3,073
North America	30,730	3,049	27,680	20,886	18,015	2,871	6,793
Total	82,782	10,821	71,952	56,463	50,878	5,585	15,494

forest areas and temporarily converting these areas into new farmland – alone accounted for 60 percent of total deforestation; and according to Myers, the scope of shifting agriculture can be expected to grow rapidly.

Hence, there is no evidence suggesting that there have been any major changes requiring a review of the findings presented by the Enquete Commission on "Preventive Measures to Protect the Earth's Atmosphere" in its third report: i.e. deforestation is still believed to account for about 10 percent of the greenhouse effect due to CO_2 emissions, and for another 5 percent due to emissions of other trace gases. The amount of carbon released by the conversion of forest areas into farmland is estimated to range between about 0.7 and 1.7 Gt (of a total of between 7.2 and 7.6 Gt C), of which 0.011 to 0.053 Gt of carbon is released in the form of methane. In addition, annual nitrogen emissions range between 0.007 and 0.017 Gt (65). Since the beginning of the industrial revolution, atmospheric carbon concentrations have increased from 275 ppm to 355 ppm. About half of this increase is due to CO_2 emissions caused by deforestation.

A more precise quantification of the radiatively active trace gas emissions released by deforestation depends on the determination of the amount of carbon stored. It is estimated that between 600 and 1,000 Gt of carbon is stored in terrestrial biomass. Depending on the physiognomic and biological character of the forest areas involved, however, the amount of carbon stored varies widely (57, cf. Table 2.6).

The amount of carbon released also depends on the degree of human interventions (cf. Table 2.7). Open forests, for instance, are usually degraded as a result of overgrazing, excessive logging, etc., while closed tropical forests tend to be completely cut down. A third limiting factor is the fact that deforestation is no longer restricted to tropical forests. Large-scale deforestation now seems to be common in Canada and Sibiria, too.

There is no clear scientific understanding yet about the question as to what direct effects deforestation has on the albedo. However, a substantial effect is likely to occur only in the case of light deforested areas that are not covered by any vegetation. Due to the succession of secondary vegetation, the albedo will once again become similar to the one above closed forests (64).

It should be emphasised that tropical deforestation has a particularly negative impact on the regional climate. Tropical deforestation has adverse effects not only on the water balance and the nutrient balance but also on the soil fertility and the development of adjacent forest regions. In addition, forest fires lead to high ozone concentrations in the troposphere above and in some cases also to photochemical smog. The adverse effects

Tabelle 2.6: *Living and Dead Biomass, Organic Matter in the Soil, and Microbial Biomass in the Most Important Global Vegetation Types*

	Tropical forests	Temperate forests	Boreal forests	Savannah land	Temperate grass-land	Tundra
Surface area (million km^2)	24.5	12.5	12.0	15.0	9.0	8.0
Living biomass (g C/m^2)	18,000	14,000	9,000	1,800	1,440	250
Litter (g C/m^2)	710	368	250	360	667	75
Soils (g C/m^2)	13,000	9,000	15,000	5,400	23,000	22,000
Soils (g N/m^2)	816	640	1,100	333	2,100	1,125
Microbial biomass (g C/m^2)	50	110	35	60	215	20
Microbial biomass (g N/m^2)	2	14	2.5	8.7	51	1
Microbial conversion (years)	0.07	0.30	0.14	0.17	0.32	0.27

Source: Scharpenseel, 1992

Tabelle 2.7: *Total Carbon and Nitrogen Compound Emissions Released by Fires*

	Carbon released (Gt per year)	Nitrogen released (Gt per year)
Shifting agriculture	0.5–1.0	0.005–0.01
Permanent deforestation	0.2–0.7	0.002–0.007
Savannah fires	0.3–1.6	0.002–0.01
Firewood	0.3–0.6	0.002–0.003
Agricultural waste	0.5–0.8	0.005–0.016
Total	1.8–4.7	0.015–0.046

Source: Andreae, 1991

of tropical deforestation on the natural potential of the regions concerned are much more severe than the impact on the global climate.

2.3.3 Agriculture

Worldwide, agriculture contributes to radiatively active trace gas emissions, in some cases even to a considerable extent (cf. Table 2.4). Identifying the emission rates of specific trace gases is difficult in many cases because agriculture invariably acts as both a source and a sink of the various substances involved.

As far as radiatively active gas emissions from the agricultural sector are concerned, a distinction must be made between directly and indirectly acting gases. The former category includes the carbon compounds CO_2 and CH_4, as well as N_2O from the group of nitrogen compounds. These gases are released when forest areas are cleared by fires to be subsequently used as farmland, as well as in cattle feedlots, rice paddies and after the use of nitrogen-based fertiliser. All of these gases directly add to the greenhouse effect, and N_2O additionally contributes towards ozone depletion.

Emissions of indirectly acting trace gases such as NO_x and NH_3 are caused by cattle feedlots but also by the activity of microorganisms in soils and water, following the use of nitrogen fertiliser. CO emissions are mainly released during the burning of biomass. There is growing evidence proving that the increasing, and in some cases excessive, use of industrial and organic fertiliser is responsible for the increase in N_2O emissions (see Chapter 2.3.3.1).

NO_x and NH_3 lead to soil acidification and eutrophication of terrestrial and aquatic ecosystems. Nitrogen oxides promote the development of phytotoxic tropospheric ozone. The damage to, and destabilisation of, the ecosystems, in turn, have adverse effects on the climate because sinks of CO_2 and other gases are destroyed in the process.

2.3.3.1 *Directly acting radiative trace gases*

Carbon dioxide (CO_2)

Land use changes in agriculture between 1860 and 1980 cumulatively accounted for about 50 percent of global man-made CO_2 emissions. Since then, the energy sector has been gaining in importance and now predominates with much higher overall CO_2 emissions, while agriculture plays a secondary role (20–30 percent in 1990) (66). Emissions from biotic sources total 1.6±1.0 Gt of carbon per year (corresponding to 5.86±3.67 Gt of CO_2 per year) (67). The overwhelming part of these emissions is released during the burning of biomass and changes in land use.

Of a total land surface of 130 million square kilometers in 1991, 15 million square kilometers were used as farmland, 32 million square kilometers were used as pasture land, and 41 million square kilometers were used for forestry. Table 2.8 shows the increase in the surface area used for human activities in the past 110 years.

To a large extent, biomass burning can be attributed directly or indirectly to agriculture and pasture farming. This includes activities such as clearing and managing forests, savannah fires, energy supply (heating, cooking, etc.) and burning agricultural waste.

In the context of the conversion of tropical forests into pasture land or other types of farmland, biomass is burnt in two stages: a large part of the forest biomass is first of all burnt when fire is set to the forests to clear them; subsequently, the areas concerned are burnt in regular intervals for agricultural reasons (preservation, pest control). This type of agricultural land use today is by far the most common. For global emissions, agriculturally induced fires (e.g.. in savannah regions) are much more significant than fires set to forests to clear them. In 1990, the CO_2 emissions caused by forest fires amounted to 987 million tonnes, while savannah fires produced as much as 2,047 million tonnes of CO_2 emissions (69).

In addition, other radiatively active trace gases – i.e. methane (CH_4), nitrous oxide (N_2O), nitrogen oxides (NO_x), carbon monoxide (CO), and hydrocarbons (CH) – are also released when biomass is burnt.

Furthermore, the soils are affected by slash-and-burn practices. When natural forest areas are converted into farmland, the amount of carbon

Table 2.8: Land Use Changes in the Past
(million km²)

Category	Inventory		Rate of change 1882–1991
	1882	1991	
Arable land	8.6	15.0	174 %
Grassland and pastures	15.0	32.0	213 %
Woodland and forest .	52.0	41.0	–21 %

Source: Norse, 1991 (68)

fixed in biomass per surface unit is reduced by a factor of between 20 and 100, and the difference is released in the form of CO_2 during the burning and microbial decomposition of the cleared biomass, or by increased mineralisation of soil organic matter. Additional carbon losses are caused by the erosion of exposed soils. The change in land use also leads to changes in the exchange of trace gases between soils and the atmosphere, in terms of both the types and volumes. Changes in the nutrients input and in the pH value affect the microflora and the microfauna. A new equilibrium develops as a function of agricultural measures applied (fertilisation, grazing, erosion control, etc.). It is only to a limited extent that agriculture can be regarded as a CO_2 sink. It is true that CO_2 is fixed again in plant biomass and in the humus of the soils; on balance, however, the carbon content is much lower than in primary forests or in managed forests.

In addition to biomass burning and changing source and sink conditions, increasingly intensive farming methods are also associated with fossil fuel consumption. In the western part of the Federal Republic of Germany, the production of mineral fertiliser, as well as the use of agricultural machinery, warehouses and cold chains involve 25.2 million tonnes of CO_2 emissions, which corresponds to 3 percent of the CO_2 emissions from the other economic sectors (70).

In the Federal Republic of Germany, CO_2 emissions due to biomass burning and land use changes play a secondary role only. Hence, there are only two options for German agriculture to reduce CO_2 emissions: conserving energy in agricultural activities, as well as generating and using renewable energy sources.

Methane (CH_4)

The annual increase in methane concentrations by between 1 and 2 percent is mainly due to human activities. In fact, it follows world population growth. Because of methodological problems, some of the data collected with regard to methane emission volumes vary widely. According to the latest estimate, the sum of all CH_4 emissions (including natural and man-made sources) amounts to 500 million tonnes per year (67). Agriculture is believed to account for roughly 70 to 80 percent of total emissions (71).

The most important agricultural sources of CH_4 emissions are rice paddies, cattle feedlots and biomass burning (see Table 2.9).

Rice paddies are overwhelmingly (90 percent) found in the tropical and subtropical regions of Asia, while a much smaller percentage is found in Latin America, Africa and Australia. In the flooded soils of the rice

Table 2.9:   Methan (CH₄)

Atmospheric lifetime	8–12 years
Annual rate of increase	1–2 percent
Annual global emissions	500 mn t
Man-made sources:	
Rice paddies	20–100 mn t
Animal farming	60–100 mn t
Burnt biomass	55–100 mn t
Waste	20– 35 mn t

Source: Bouwman, 1991 (72)

paddies, organic matter is decomposed anaerobically (in the absence of air) by certain groups of bacteria (methanogenic archaeobacteria), which produce methane in the process. A large part of this methane is already oxidised on the water surface by methanotrophic bacteria. Nevertheless, between 20 and 100 million tonnes of methane are released annually.

In view of the continuing population growth predicted for the next few decades, rice demand can be expected to increase substantially. Estimates of the International Rice Research Institute (IRRI) in Manila/Philippines suggest that world rice production will have to grow from 519 million tonnes in 1990 to at least 556 million tonnes by the year 2000, and to 758 million tonnes by the year 2020 (which corresponds to an increase by 46 percent overall, or by 1.5 percent annually). The more intensive cultivation methods required to achieve this increase will lead to higher emissions (73).

However, methane emission rates from rice paddies are very much dependent on irrigation management, the number of crops per year, fertilising conditions, and last but not least, the rice varieties used.

According to optimistic estimates, it might be possible – in spite of higher production volumes – to achieve a stagnation of emission rates by the application of new, improved cultivation techniques, more efficient water management, and the selection of "low-emission" rice varieties. The implementation of these plans requires a fast, interdisciplinary and integrated development concept.

In the developed countries, methane emissions from cattle farming amount to between 60 and 100 million tonnes annually. These methane emissions are overwhelmingly (90 percent) due to the anaerobic decomposition of cellulose in ruminants. Since 1950, global meat production has quadrupled, while the world population has only doubled in this period of time. A considerable part of the feed needed for cattle farming in the industrialised nations is imported from developing countries.

The methane emissions calculated for the Federal Republic of Germany amount to about 1.2 million tonnes of CH_4 per year (74). Table 2.10 lists the emission rate for the Federal Republic of Germany, as well as for other countries.

The volume of methane produced depends on the type and the quantity of animal feed used. Intensive (large-scale) animal husbandry, involving the

Table 2.10: Methane Emissions from Animal Farming, 1990
('000 tonnes CH_4 per year)

	Country / Region	Total	Percentage
1	Belgium	168	2.8
2	Denmark	138	2.3
3	France	1,326	22.4
4	Germany (Federal Republic and GDR)	1,218	20.6
5	Greece	159	2.7
6	Ireland	353	6.0
7	Italy	608	10.3
8	Luxembourg	6	0.1
9	Netherlands	389	6.6
10	Portugal	128	2.2
11	Spain	516	8.7
12	United Kingdom	905	15.3
	Total	5 914	100,0
1–12	EC	5 914	8.0
13	Non-EC OECD Europe	1,477	2.0
14	OECD Pacific Region	3,787	5.1
15	Non OECD Europe	2,310	3.1
16	USSR	7,577	10.2
17	North America	6,738	9.1
18	Latin America	12,613	17.0
19	Africa	9,565	12.9
20	Middle East	1,212	1.6
21	Asian planned economies	6,171	8.3
22	South and Southeast Asia	16,736	22.6
	Total	74,100	100.0

Source: Bouwman, 1991 (75)

use of correspondingly high-energy animal feed, leads to maximum methane production rates. Energy balance studies have shown that up to 12 percent of the animal feed energy is lost in the form of methane emissions (76).

The options available to the Federal Republic of Germany to reduce methane emissions include adapting animal feeding methods, reducing the number of animals and the scope of large-scale animal farming.

Methane emissions due to biomass burning when forests are set ablaze in order to clear the land for farming, and due to natural forest and steppe fires amount to between 55 and 100 million tonnes annually (72). It will continue to be difficult to control these fires.

An additional source of methane emissions – which has probably been underestimated in the past – is human and animal waste. Recent data suggest that global emissions from this source range between 20 and 35 million tonnes of CH_4 per year. The anaerobic decomposition of waste in landfills accounts for a major part of the methane emissions from this source (67). According to a recent study, methane emissions from waste and sewage sludge landfills in the Federal Republic of Germany amount to as much as 1.1 to 1.6 million tonnes of CH_4 (80). Options available to reduce these emissions include waste prevention, reduction and recycling, as well as modern landfill management, in particular sealing the landfill so that it is gastight and recovering the gas emissions for energy purposes. Other sources of methane emissions are local sewage treatment plants, leakages from biogas plants, and other anaerobic treatment processes (i.e. processes that occur in the absence of air).

Nitrous oxide (N_2O)

The data available to date are not sufficiently reliable yet to permit a breakdown of nitrous oxide emissions by source. However, it is safe to say that the relative importance of the combustion of fossil fuels as a source of N_2O emissions has been overestimated. It is likely, therefore, that most of the annual N_2O emissions of between 3.0 and 4.5 million tonnes (78) are caused by agriculture.

N_2O has two radiative effects: first of all, it is the most important ozone depleting compound after the CFCs. The lifetime of N_2O molecules is very long (between 130 and 150 years). At high altitudes, N_2O is broken down by photodecomposition. This process leads to the development of reactive nitrogen oxides which contribute to ozone depletion. Currently, the CFCs are mainly involved in ozone depletion. However, after the phase-out of CFC production, a similarly high ozone depletion potential might develop by a cumulative increase in N_2O concentrations (79).

In addition, nitrous oxide is a radiatively active gas which exacerbates global warming. So far, its contribution in this field has been estimated to be 5 percent (10). The specific risk which this gas represents is once again its long lifetime, which suggests that it will have an increasing impact on global warming (80). N_2O is produced both by anaerobic processes (denitrification and nitratammonification, i.e. decomposition of nitrate in the soil) and, to a lesser extent, by an aerobic process (nitrification, i.e. nitrate production in the soil). These processes are caused by certain groups of bacteria.

It is safe to say that the increase in N_2O emissions (from 0.2 to 0.3 percent in the past decade) is due to the increasing and in some cases even excessive application of industrial and organic nitrogen fertiliser. Since 1960, global nitrogen fertiliser consumption has increased by 6.8 percent annually; between 1977 and 1987 alone, consumption rose by a total of about 50 percent (81) (76). Of the total fertiliser nitrogen used, 3.2 percent is released as N_2O (78). Increasing cultivation of leguminosae (involving nitrogen fixation by symbiotic nodule bacteria) also contributes towards rising emissions.

In global terms, there is a considerable imbalance in the use of fertiliser, with substantial surpluses in the nitrogen balance of the industrialised nations. In this context, it should be borne in mind that surplus nitrogen contaminates surface water and groundwater resources, and hence, is released as N_2O from apparently "natural" ecosystems. In the final analysis, all man-made nitrogen inputs will eventually show up in the atmosphere as N_2 or N_2O following denitrification.

If the world population continues to grow, global fertiliser consumption can be expected to rise. However, it is very difficult to predict the rate of this increase. Because of the hazard potential of N_2O, this sector will have to be watched carefully. For this reason, the industrialised nations should be urged to reduce the amount of fertiliser they use, to balance their nitrogen budgets and to make greater use of extensive farming.

Other radiatively active gases

Other radiatively active gases – albeit with a marginal impact on the greenhouse effect – are carbon monoxide (CO) and carbonyl sulphide (COS). The former is released when biomass is burnt, accounting for a total of 350 million tonnes of CO emissions per year (82). CO interferes with other atmospheric components such as CH_4, OH and O_3, thus leading to other perturbations of the system via feedback effects.

The main sources of marine carbonyl sulphide emissions are coastal and shelf areas of the oceans, where organic sulphur compounds are decomposed by photochemical processes (83). By increasing biomass production (algae bloom periods), man-made inputs of nutrients due to animal farming and fertiliser use might contribute to a substantial increase in emissions.

2.3.3.2 Indirectly acting trace gases

Ammonia (NH_3) and nitrogen oxides (NO_x)

As already mentioned, the nitrogen surpluses caused by intensive farming practices and animal husbandry and their associated emissions contribute towards climate change.

Gaseous nitrogen compounds which are formed in agriculture include not only nitrous oxide but also ammonia (NH_3) and nitrogen oxides (NO_x).

Both gases are introduced – via the air and via water – into natural and quasi-natural ecosystems which are accustomed to low nitrogen concentrations. Initially this leads to the eutrophication of terrestrial (forests, heaths, swamps) and aquatic communities (inland and coastal waters). Eventually, however, these additional man-made nitrogen inputs will be denitrified, and some of this nitrogen will reach the atmosphere in the form of nitrous oxide and thus exacerbate global warming.

Another adverse effect is the acidification of soils and water resources. Acidification, as well as higher nitrogen emissions and increasing concentrations of air pollutants (O_3, SO_2) have now been identified as the major causes of the forest dieback in the Northern Hemisphere.

Ecosystems are severely damaged by these effects, and a flexible adaptation of the stressed ecosystems in response to climate change becomes more difficult.

Ammonia (NH_3)

Agriculture accounts for 90 percent of national (German), continental (Western European) and global NH_3 emissions; and 80 percent of these agricultural emissions are due to animal farming. Total emissions in the Federal Republic of Germany amount to 528,000 tonnes of NH_3 annually. Sources of ammonia emissions are stables, pastures, as well as the storage and application of organic fertiliser.

Nitrogen monoxide (NO) and nitrogen dioxide (NO_x)

NO and NO_2 – jointly referred to as NO_x – are produced when forest areas are cleared and when secondary cultivated savannah areas are burnt. In tropical regions, these fires may lead to high nitrogen oxide emissions, and thus to ozone concentrations that are comparable to those found in the photo-smog areas in the Northern Hemisphere (83). Nitrogen oxides are also produced by the same microbiological processes that also lead to the production of N_2O (denitrification, nitrification). The rates at which the three gases are produced vary with soil conditions. NO_x releases are substantially stimulated by the use of nitrogen fertiliser.

Ammonia and nitrogen oxide emissions could be cut down by reducing livestocks, using other animal feed and reducing the use of manure. In the Federal Republic of Germany, considerable reductions of both NH_3 and NO_x emissions could be achieved by optimising the use of nitrogen fertiliser and the storage and application of organic fertiliser. This would be desirable not only for ecological but also for economic reasons.

2.3.4 Chlorofluorocarbons, halons and chemically related substitutes

2.3.4.1 Background

Chlorofluorocarbons and halons are mainly responsible for stratospheric ozone depletion; at the same time, they are radiatively active gases which exacerbate man-made global warming. Against the background of increasing ozone depletion (see Chapter 3.1), the international community of nations is called upon – in cooperation with the chemical industry – to stop the production of ozone-depleting substances immediately (see Chapter 5).

Fully halogenated CFCs and halons are highly inert chemical compounds which are broken down almost exclusively by photodecomposition in the stratosphere. Partially halogenated compounds (H-CFCs) contain not only carbon and halogen atoms but also hydrogen atoms. The effect of the latter is that most of these compounds are broken down in the troposphere. Hence, their ozone depletion and global warming potentials are lower than those of the CFCs used in the past. Nevertheless, the ODPs and GWPs of partially halogenated compounds should not be underestimated.

While fluorocarbons (FCs) do not contribute to ozone depletion, they do add to the greenhouse effect. H-CFCs and FCs are currently being discussed as possible alternatives to replace CFCs. In the case of most of these substances, however, the tests conducted to establish their environmental safety (toxicity, mutagenic and carcinogenic effects) have not yet been concluded. Partially halogenated H-CFCs should not be used more extensively, however, because of their global warming and ozone depletion potentials.

Table 2.2 in Chapter 2.2.1.3 shows the current concentrations, as well as the annual growth rates and the mean atmospheric lifetimes of the most important CFCs, H-CFCs and halons. In addition, this table also contains estimates of the ozone depletion and global warming potentials of these substances.

2.3.4.2 Production and consumption

The emission rates of CFCs, halons and of chemically related substitutes are currently frought with a high degree of uncertainty. Only in exceptional cases has the chemical industry been prepared to disclose precise data on production and consumption volumes. Hence, it is impossible to establish a balance between the consumption volumes of ozone-depleting substances, their emission rates as well as the atmospheric concentrations measured.

Fully and partially halogenated chlorofluorocarbons

Table 2.11 gives an overview of the 1989 production and consumption volumes of the most important fully and partially halogenated chlorofluorocarbons within the EC. According to this overview, the two predominant substances were CFC-11 and CFC-12. About 76 percent of CFC-11 was used for the production of foams, while CFC-12 was primarily used in automotive air-conditioning systems. The percentage shares of the various CFC applications vary considerably from country to country in the European Community.

Figure 2.15 shows the trends in CFC production volumes worldwide, in the EC and in the Federal Republic of Germany (including the new federal states). As this figure illustrates, there has only been a very minor decline in global CFC production, relative to 1986, while EC production has decreased by 35 percent and production in the Federal Republic of Germany has dropped by 49 percent.

Halons

Halon production volumes have fallen from 71,200 tonnes in 1986 to 54,300 tonnes in 1990, albeit not continuously. According to data published by the Federal Ministry of the Environment, halon production in the Federal Republic of Germany (including the new federal states) amounted to 18,100 tonnes in 1986 and to 15,900 tonnes in 1990. (These

Table 2.11: CFC Production, Import and Export Volumes in the EC, 1989
(tonnes)

CFC	11	12	113	114	115	H-CFC
Production (actual production, excluding imports, sales between EC CFC producers, and production of intermediates) ...	165,087	124,073	68,040	6,346	8,944	61,157
Imports from non-EC countries	—	46	387	—	1,167	n.s.
Sales within the EC .	108,507	71,131	44,578	4,123	3,478	32,299
Total exports to countries outside the EC (including sales between non-EC CFC producers)	53,201	53,467	22,341	1,899	6,559	n.s.
Stocks as per 1 Jan. 1989	6,865	8,453	7,201	807	766	n.s.
Stocks as per 31 Dec. 1989	10,333	8,127	8,799	1,135	849	n.s.
Percentage EC/ world ratio						
– production	54		27		63	28
– consumption ...	36		18		25	15

n.s. = not specified

Source: Federal Ministry of the Environment, from: Enquete Commission, Third Report

data have been converted into weighted tonnes, i.e. the respective production volumes have been multiplied by the ozone depletion potential standardised in the Montreal Protocol, and hence correspond to equivalent CFC volumes with an ozone depletion potential of 1).

Table 2.12 shows estimates of 1986 halon consumption volumes in the European Community, the Federal Republic of Germany, the United

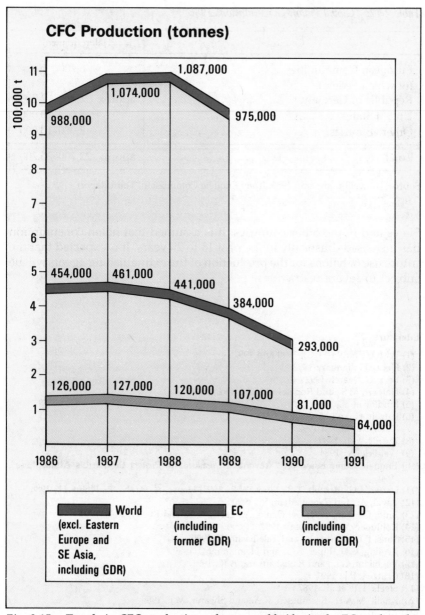

Fig. 2.15: Trends in CFC production volumes worldwide, in the EC, and in the Federal Republic of Germany (including the new federal states),
Source: Federal Ministry of the Environment

Table 2.12:   Global Halon Consumption, 1986

Countries	Halon (tonnen)
European Communities	6,700
(of which Federal	
Republic of Germany)	approx. 1,300– 2,000
United States	8,000–10,000
Other countries	8,000–10,000
Total	approx. 22,700–26,700

Source: Umweltbundesamt, 1989, from: Enquete Commission, Third Report

States and in the other countries. It is assumed that halon consumption has increased drastically in the past 15 to 20 years. It is expected that the future use of halons for the production of fire extinguishing agents will be subject to severe restrictions.

Literature

(1) WMO/UNEP (IPCC), 1990 and 1992
(2) Flohn, H., January 1992
(3) Berz, G., March 1992
(4) Halpert, M.S., and Ropelewski, C.F. (ed.), 1991
(5) Bradley et al., 1987
(6) Patzelt, G. and M. Aellen, 1990
(7) Kuhn, M., March 1992
(8) Zwally, H.J., 1989
(9) Weidick, A., 1984
(10) Enquete Commission on "Preventive Measures to Protect the Earth's Atmosphere", 1990
(11) Gaffen, D.J., Barnett, T.B., Elliot, W.P., 1991; Hense, A., Krahe, P., Flohn, H., 1988
(12) Raval, A., and Ramanathan, V., 1990
(13) Rind, D. et al., 1991; Del Genio, A., Lacis, A.A., and Ruedy, R.A., 1991
(14) Kohlmaier, G.H., January 1992
(15) Tans, P.P., Fung, I.Y., and Takahashi, T., 1990
(16) Keeling, C.D., Piper, S.C., and Heimann, M., 1989
(17) Vaghjiani, G.L., and Ravishankara, A.R., 1991
(18) Crutzen, P.J., 1991
(19) Steele, L.P. et al., 1987
(20) Khalil, M.A.K., Rasmussen, R.A., and Shearer, M.J., 1989
(21) Khalil, M.A.K., and Rasmussen, R.A., 1990
(22) Zellner, R., January 1992
(23) WMO/UNEP Global Ozone Research and Monitoring Project, no. 25, 1992
(24) WMO/UNEP Global Ozone Research and Monitoring Project, no. 18, 1989

(25) Mather, J.H., and Brune, W.H., 1990

(26) Pitari, G., Visconti, G., and Rizi, V., 1991

(27) Volz-Thomas, A., and Kley, D., 1988

(28) Lacis, A.A., Wuebbles, D.J., and Logan, J.A., 1990

(29) Brunke, E.-G., Scheel, H.E., and Seiler, W., 1990

(30) Hofmann, D.J., 1990; Hofmann, D.J., 1991

(31) Jäger, H., 1991; Jäger, H., January 1992

(32) Husar, R.B. et al., 1979

(33) Graßl, H., 1992; Coakley, J.A., Bernstein, R.L., and Durkee, P.A., 1987

(34) Hansen, J. et al., 1992

(35) Schumann, U., 1992

(36) Harrison, E.F. et al., 1990

(37) Sagan, C., Toon, O.B., and Pollack, J.B., 1979

(38) Foukal, P., and Lean, J., 1990

(39) Gilliland, R.L., 1982

(40) Milankovic, M., 1941; Berger, A., 1980

(41) Sieferle, 1982

(42) Marchetti, 1980

(43) Federal Ministry of Economics, 1991; GECR (Global Environmental Change Report), 1991

(44) IEA, 1991

(45) Süddeutsche Zeitung, 3 June 1991

(46) WEC, 1989

(47) Federal Ministry of Economics, 1991; Federal Statistics Office, 1990

(48) Federal Ministry of the Environment/Interministerial Task Force, 1991

(49) Left-hand columns: German Federal Government, 1992; right-hand columns: Federal Ministry of Economics, 1991; DIW, 1991; calculations by the Enquete Commission

(50) Federal Ministry of Economics, 1991; 1991 data: Schiffer, 1992; calculations by the Enquete Commission

(51) Federal Ministry of the Environment/Interministerial Task Force, 1991

(52) Prognos, 1991

(53) Federal Ministry of Economics, 1991

(54) Commission of the European Communities, 1991

(55) United Nations, 1990

(56) BUND, 1992

(57) Scharpenseel, 1992

(58) Schumann, U., 1990

(59) Schumann, U., 1992

(60) Myers, 1991

(61) FAO, 1985

(62) FAO, 1988

(63) FAO, 1992

(64) Graßl, H., 1992

(65) WMO/UNEP (IPCC), 1992

(66) Bouwman, A.F., 1991, p. 207

(67) WMO/UNEP (IPCC), 1992

(68) Norse, D., 1991

(69) Bouwman, A.F., 1991, p. 248

(70) Haider, K., Sauerbeck, D., 1991

(71) Bouwman, A.F., 1990

(72) Bouwman, A.F., 1991, p. 216

(73) Neue, H.U., 1991; IRRI, 1990

(74) FAL, 1990

(75) Bouwman, A.F., 1991, p. 239
(76) FAL, 1990
(77) Graßl et al., 1991
(78) WMO/UNEP (IPCC), 1992
(79) Crutzen, P., Heinloth, K., 1991
(80) Bouwman, A.F., 1991, p. 216
(81) Bouwman, A.F., 1991, p. 219; Sauerbeck, D., 1991, p. 271
(82) Bouwman, A.F., 1991, p. 248
(83) Andreae, M., 1991, p. 4

3. The Scope of the Future Threat Potential

Summary

Man-made stratospheric ozone depletion is much greater than had been assumed up to a few years ago. Ozone losses are most pronounced during the winter and spring months (about 6 percent per decade). This increase, which represents an acceleration of the trend by another 2 percent per decade as compared to previous analyses, is due to the greater ozone depletion observed during the Eighties. In terms of its "depth" and its expanse, the 1991 Antarctic ozone hole was comparable to the ozone holes observed in 1987, 1989 and 1990.

In the winter of 1991-92, an unusually low total ozone abundance was measured over large areas of the Northern Hemisphere; in Europe, the ozone levels measured in the months of December, January and February were up to 10 percent below the long-term mean.

Current findings suggest that all chemically induced ozone losses are due to the stratospheric abundance of chlorine and bromine compounds. The overwhelming part of the increase in stratospheric concentrations of these two elements is caused by man-made emissions.

It is expected that the ozone trends observed will continue to speed up in the next few decades. An immediate phase-out of CFC production is therefore indispensable.

In the next 100 to 200 years, the man-made greenhouse effect will have a major impact on the global climate. Based on the assumption that man-made emissions of radiatively active trace gases will not be substantially reduced, the mean global temperature can be expected to rise by an average of 0.3 °C per decade. When equivalent CO_2 concentrations will have doubled (about 2025), the mean global temperature will be about 1.5 °C above its current level.

Warming will be more pronounced above the continents than above the oceans. At higher latitudes, there will be a general increase in precipitation while, at mid-latitudes, precipitation is expected to increase in winter and to decrease in summer.

To some extent, the effects of global climate change can now be demonstrated on the basis of data measured. In addition, major progress has been achieved in assessing regional threat potentials. Climate change is likely to have a more severe impact on the countries of the South than on the industrialised nations.

The most immediate threat emanates from an increasing frequency of climatically induced catastrophes (e.g. tropical cyclones), which has already become manifest. In future, there will also be a much higher frequency of prolonged droughts alternating with heavy rainfall, which will mainly jeopardise semi-arid regions.

The expected rise in sea level by between 70 and 100 cm during the next century will increase the number of flood disasters and lead to permanently flooded fertile coastal plains, some of which are densely populated. Deltas and estuaries of large rivers will be particularly at risk in this context. In addition, some Pacific island states will suffer considerable losses of land, and there is a risk that parts of these island states will become uninhabitable.

Both the extent and the rate of climate change will overtax the adaptability of forests and natural ecosystems. There is a risk that ecosystems will collapse on a large scale, which will have severe ecological and socio-economic consequences.

Agricultural production will be particularly jeopardised by climatic shifts. It is above all in zones with continental climates that soils can be expected to dessicate, which will lead to corresponding degradation phenomena (e.g. increasing salinity, erosion). An increasing frequency of extreme climatic events and greater proliferation of plant diseases and pests in a warmer climate will have an adverse impact on yields. However, the fertilising effect associated with increasing atmospheric CO_2 concentrations will hardly affect plant growth. Against the background of rapid population growth, there is a risk that world food supply will be severely compromised.

Another climatically induced threat may be an acceleration of microbial decomposition of dead organic matter in a warmer climate. The additional atmospheric carbon dioxide emissions caused by this phenomenon might reach a magnitude that would be comparable to the emissions due to the combustion of fossil fuels, which might substantially exacerbate the greenhouse effect.

3.1 Stratospheric Ozone Depletion

3.1.1 Current status and future trends

In terms of its "depth" and its expanse, the 1991 Antarctic ozone hole was comparable to the ozone holes observed in 1987, 1989 and 1990. The minimum vertical column ozone density amounted to 110 Dobson units, which corresponds to an ozone loss of 60 percent, relative to the ozone levels measured in the late Seventies. In 1991, the ozone hole extended over about 6.5 percent of the total area of the Southern Hemisphere.

The mean stratospheric chlorine mixing ratio, which is mainly determined by man-made chlorine emissions in the form of CFCs, is put at between 3.3 and 3.5 ppbv (1). Even if all the parties to the Montreal Protocol comply with the strengthened provisions (adopted at their second meeting in London in 1990), it will not be possible to prevent chlorine concentrations from rising to a level of 4.1 ppbv by the year 2000. If the parties to the Protocol strictly adhere to its provisions, model predictions suggest that the mean stratospheric chlorine mixing ratio will not return to its pre-Antarctic-ozone-hole level of 2 ppbv before the middle of the next century.

In the past 10 years, stratospheric ozone concentrations have decreased by between 5 and 10 percent (1). Figure 3.1 shows the ozone depletion rates as percentages per decade for various latitudes and seasons, based on TOMS satellite data collected between November 1978 and March 1991. While there are striking seasonal differences in ozone trends in the Northern Hemisphere, seasonal variability in the Southern Hemisphere is more limited (except for Antarctica). However, ozone depletion as such is more pronounced in the Southern Hemisphere than in the Northern Hemisphere, whereas there are are no major ozone losses in the tropics. Stratospheric ozone depletion will continue in the next few years. In fact, it is very likely that the size of the Antarctic ozone hole will double in the next 10 to 20 years (2).

Model calculations involving scenarios have shown that if the CFC production phase-out is accelerated by three years, for instance, this would not only reduce the expected peak level of the mean stratospheric chlorine mixing ratio from 4.1 to 3.9 ppbv, but it would also accelerate the decrease in chlorine concentrations to 3 ppbv by 10 years, and to 2 ppbv by 7 years (1).

During the 1991-92 winter, unusually low total ozone levels were observed in large parts of the Northern Hemisphere. The lowest levels were measured above Europe (3), where – following "normal" behaviour

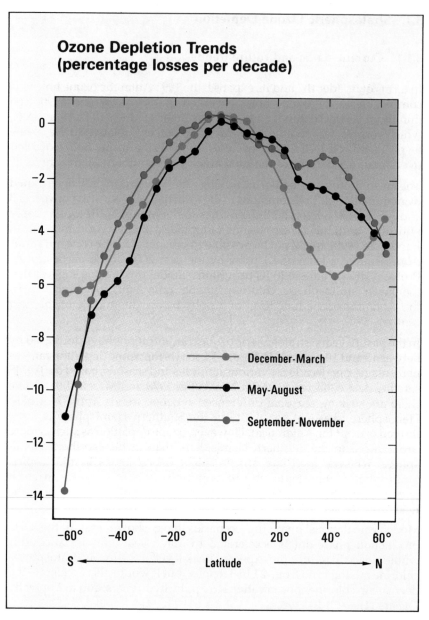

Fig. 3.1: *Percentage ozone depletion trends per decade as a function of latitude and seasons, based on TOMS data collected between November 1978 and March 1991.*
Source: WMO Report 25, 1992

in November – vertical column densities were 10 percent below the multi-annual mean (Hohenpeißenberg) in the months that followed (December, January, February). Similar observations were also made at the stations in Lindenberg and Ny Ålesund (Spitzbergen, 79° N) in the framework of the European Arctic Stratosphere Ozone Experiment (EASOE). While these changes in ozone concentrations occurred at all altitudes of the stratosphere, they were most pronounced in the lower stratosphere, i.e. at an altitude of between 13 and 18 kilometers.

Figure 3.2 shows the TOMS satellite measurements of total column ozone densities above the Northern Hemisphere on 18 January 1992 and 4 March 1992. In the core of this ozone-depleted area, total column ozone ranged only between 200 and 220 Dobson units; even above Central Europe, including the area above the Federal Republic of Germany, ozone levels did not exceed 260 Dobson units. Outside this area, ozone concentrations were at the level of the long-term mean, i.e. about 400 Dobson units. In early March (see Fig. 3.2), total column ozone was still at a relative minimum above Europe; however, in the course of February 1992, ozone concentrations temporarily returned to normal levels (3).

The low ozone levels above Europe coincided – in terms of both time and space – with a pronounced and persistent high-pressure area above the British Isles. This suggests that this has been directly due to meteorologically induced dynamic processes. It is very likely that these processes – combined with heterogeneous chemical processes – are responsible for the changes in stratospheric ozone distribution and concentrations. This is in agreement with the almost normal total ozone distribution observed in the Northern Hemisphere outside the area where low ozone levels were measured. According to the TOMS satellite data, mean total ozone abundance above the entire area affected was between 5 and 10 percent below the corresponding 1987–88 mean. What is interesting in this context is that, while minimum diurnal ozone levels were comparable in both periods, diurnal ozone peaks were considerably lower in 1992.

There is general agreement about the fact that the major ozone losses observed above Antarctica in spring are due to heterogeneous chemical processes which occur on the surfaces of polar stratospheric clouds (PSCs). During these processes, nitrogen oxides (mainly NO_2) are bound and reactive chlorine compounds are released. When the sunlight returns in spring, the latter destroy the ozone in the Antarctic stratosphere by catalytic action. PSCs can only develop at temperatures of −80°C or below, which, however, have not been observed in the stratosphere above Europe. The increased rate of ozone depletion which occurred above Europe in the winter of 1991–92 therefore suggests that there must be

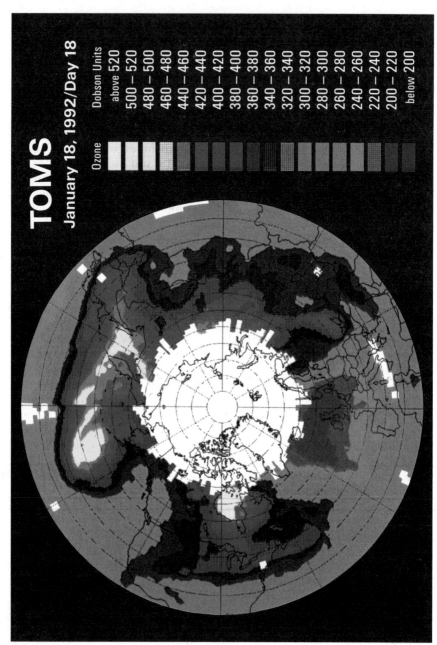

Fig. 3.2: TOMS data on total column ozone in the Northern Hemisphere on 18
January 1992 and 4 March 1992 (Krueger, A.J., 1992, personal communication)

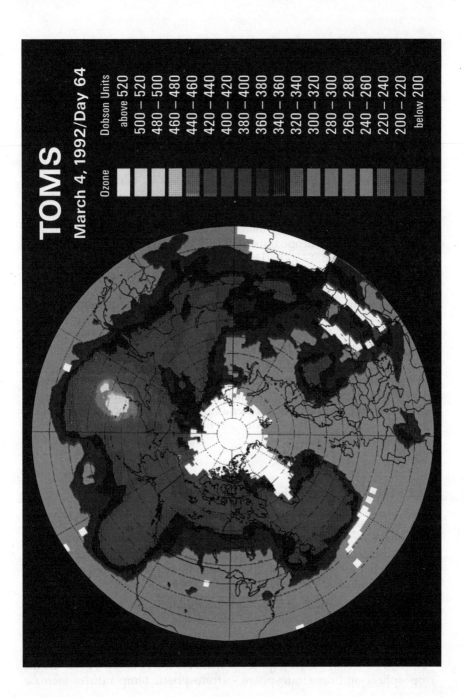

TOMS

March 4, 1992/Day 64

Ozone   Dobson Units

above 520
500 – 520
480 – 500
460 – 480
440 – 460
420 – 440
400 – 420
380 – 400
360 – 380
340 – 360
320 – 340
300 – 320
280 – 300
260 – 280
240 – 260
220 – 240
200 – 220
below 200

other ozone-depleting processes in the stratosphere. These may include heterogeneous chemical reactions occurring on the surfaces of sulphuric acid aerosol particles, which can be active worldwide since they are globally distributed in the "Junge layer" (4)(5).

Laboratory experiments have demonstrated that NO_x is removed from the gas phase (denoxification of the stratosphere) by heterogeneous chemical reactions on sulphuric acid droplets, in particular by the following reaction:

$$N_2O_5 \text{ (gas)} + H_2SO_4/H_2O \text{ (liq)} \rightarrow 2 \text{ } HNO_3/H_2SO_4 \text{ (liq)}$$

This leads to an increase in the concentrations of reactive chlorine compounds. These laboratory findings have been corroborated by observations of substantially increased ClO concentrations in the winter stratosphere above Europe outside the "Pinatubo cloud". These findings cannot be explained if – as had been assumed in the past – only gas phase chemistry was involved. The increase in the number of sulphuric acid particles caused by the eruption of the Pinatubo can be expected, therefore, to amplify stratospheric ozone depletion, and thus to exacerbate the trend observed to date. This assumption is consistent with the 10-percent drop in stratospheric ozone concentrations observed this winter above the tropics (between 10° S and 20° N), where no significant changes in total ozone had occurred previously (see above). Because of denoxification in conjunction with chlorine activation, the trend observed at northern high latitudes – i. e. total ozone reaching minimum levels in winter/spring – will also be further amplified. However, the effect of the Pinatubo eruption will peter out after a few years because of aerosol particle sedimentation.

3.1.2   Effects of stratospheric ozone depletion

The importance of stratospheric ozone depletion cannot be stressed enough. While Chapter 2.2.1.3 offered a detailed discussion of the effects of stratospheric ozone depletion on the Earth's radiation budget, the present chapter is devoted to its effects on dynamic stratospheric processes and on UV-B radiation on the Earth's surface.

When ozone is formed, short-wave solar radiation is converted into heat. It is for this reason and because of the vertical distribution of ozone that the latter controls the vertical temperature structure, and hence, the dynamic processes of the stratosphere. From its minimum of between −50° and −80°C in the tropopause – which is the boundary between the troposphere and the stratosphere – stratospheric temperatures increase with altitude until they reach a maximum of about 0° C at an altitude of 50 kilometers. Because of the resulting stable stratification, the scope for vertical air transport is relatively limited in the stratosphere. Hence, decreasing stratospheric ozone concentrations are tantamount to decreasing stability, i. e. increasing vertical air transport in the stratosphere (7).

However, another effect of decreasing stratospheric ozone levels is more alarming: At an altitude of between 20 and 30 kilometers, the stratospheric ozone layer is at its "thickest" and acts as a highly effective shield which protects the Earth from ultraviolet radiation by absorbing almost all of the solar radiation in a wavelength spectrum ranging from 230 to 320 nm (nanometers). The extremely short-wave portion of UV radiation (<290 nm) is lethal for lower organisms and for the surface cells of higher organisms. Sufficiently long exposure to so-called UV-B radiation (ranging from 290 to 320 nm in wavelength) leads to severe lesions in human beings, animals and plants. The effects of increases in UV-B radiation surface intensity on human health will include an increase in the incidence of skin cancer and of cataracts, as well as a weakening of the immune system. In countries such as Argentina, Chile, Australia and New Zealand, which are directly affected by the heterogeneous ozone depletion phenomenon above Antarctica, the effects of the exposure to increasingly intense UV-B radiation have been manifest for several years.

The increasing destruction of the protective shield in the stratosphere can also have adverse effects on phytoplankton living in ocean surface waters. Since phytoplankton is an important link in the marine food chain, this would also have a considerable impact on higher forms of marine life.

The increase in UV-B radiation intensity due to stratospheric ozone depletion has been demonstrated by data collected at the alpine Jungfrauenjoch station in Switzerland (47° N; 3,576 meters a.m.s.l.), where the intensity of this radiation range showed a linear increase of about 1 percent per year in the period between 1981 and 1989 (7).

It is possible to estimate the intensity of UV-B radiation which actually reaches the Earth's surface at sea level by means of models which take into account not only the vertical distribution of the trace gases O_3, SO_2, NO_2 and of aerosol particles in lower troposphere but also average cloud conditions (8). According to these models, UV-B radiation intensity increased by between 4 and 12 percent at mid-latitudes of both hemispheres in the period from 1979 to 1989. The mean increase in intensity calculated for Antarctica was even as high as 50 percent. For the months of September and October (when vertical column ozone densities

101

are at their lowest), the model calculations suggested increases by 140 percent. The results obtained for some of the mid-latitude industrial agglomerations with high levels of air pollution, however, went against the general trend by suggesting minor decreases in UV-B surface intensity. These decreases are due to increased scattering of radiation at aerosol particles and relatively high ozone mixing ratios in the air directly above the industrial agglomerations. It should be pointed out in this context that, at higher concentrations, tropospheric ozone has toxic effects, which is why increases in tropospheric ozone concentrations should be prevented at all costs (and also because of the impact ozone has on the climate).

In man, the ozone concentrations which are nowadays reached during "photo smog periods" in summer lead to irritation of the eyes and of the airways, and to a considerable reduction of the tidal volume (the amount of air that is inspired and expired during one respiratory cycle). Plants are even more sensitive in their response to increasing O_3 mixing ratios. In the Netherlands, exposure to photo-oxidants is currently estimated to reduce agricultural yields by as much as 3 to 5 percent (9).

3.2   Global Climate Change

Climate model calculations make it possible to predict trends as well as the scope of global climate change and its effects on specific regions. However, depending on the characteristics of the model used and depending on its "mesh size" and the assumptions made with regard to the future development of radiatively active trace gas emissions into the atmosphere, such predictions are more or less fraught with uncertainties. The best climate models currently available are global, coupled ocean/ atmosphere circulation models (10). At present, there are four different coupled ocean/atmosphere models which have been used for climate simulations extending over a period of up to 100 years (GFDL, Princeton, United States; NCAR, Boulder, United States; Hadley Centre, U. K.; Max-Planck-Institut fär Meteorologie, Hamburg, Federal Republic of Germany). The simulations performed by means of these models have led to similar results. This is remarkable because the four models vary in terms of their formulation and parametrisation and in the way the model runs are carried out (11). The results of the simulation runs are briefly described below.

In all four models, it is assumed that there will be a more or less continuous increase in atmospheric CO_2 concentrations. While this increase varies from model to model, the mean rate of increase over the entire period covered by the simulation runs is the same for all models, i.e. about 1 percent annually. Two of the five IPCC emission scenarios (A and D) were calculated by means of the Hamburg model. Figure 3.3 shows the emission trends predicted under these five scenarios for CO_2 and for the sum of all greenhouse gases (10). Scenario A ("business as usual") is based on the assumption that no action will be taken to limit the emissions of greenhouse gases. The assumptions made in the other scenarios (B, C, D, E) involve the adoption of reduction measures (which are increasingly drastic from B to E).

Based on these assumptions, the models predict that global and seasonal mean surface temperatures will increase by an average of about 0.3 °C per decade over the next 100 years. For the first few decades of this simulation run, which begins in 1985, the models predict a relatively slow temperature rise (see Fig. 3.4). This may be due, to some extent, to the specific conditions applying to the simulation run, where warming rates are calculated without taking into account the atmospheric changes which took place in the years before 1985 (cold start). Because of this cold start, there is also an unrealistic delay in the sea-level rise caused by the thermal expansion of surface water. After this cold-start phase, the models predict a mean rise of sea level by between 2 and 4 cm per decade.

The potential scope of climate change as a function of future greenhouse gas emission trends becomes much clearer, however, if one looks at the regional distribution of atmospheric surface temperatures at the end of the simulation period (the year 2085). Figure 3.5 shows the results of the Hamburg climate model (MPI) for the two IPCC emission scenarios A ("business as usual") and D (very drastic reductions of greenhouse gas emissions).

However, regional predictions are still rather uncertain because the horizontal resolution in all four models ranges between 500 and 1,000 kilometers. Nevertheless, there was relatively good agreement between the various simulation results with regard to the following predictions:

- The rise of atmospheric surface temperatures will be greater above land surfaces than above ocean surfaces. Because of interhemispherical differences in the distribution of continents, this will also lead to differences in the warming of both hemispheres. In the stratosphere, however, temperatures will generally decline.
- Warming will be least pronounced in southern high-latitude ocean areas and in the North Atlantic. In fact, the increase in surface temperatures predicted is at least 60 percent lower in these areas, compared with the results of equilibrium-response model calculations involving a (sudden) doubling of atmospheric CO_2 levels.

CO₂ and Equivalent CO₂ Emission Scenarios (IPCC)

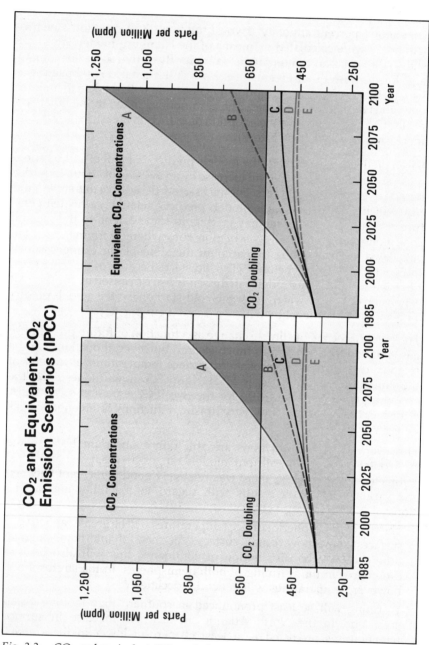

Fig. 3.3: *CO₂ and equivalent CO₂ emission scenarios of the IPCC, ranging from A ("business as usual") to D and E ("draconic reductions") (from IPCC WG I)*

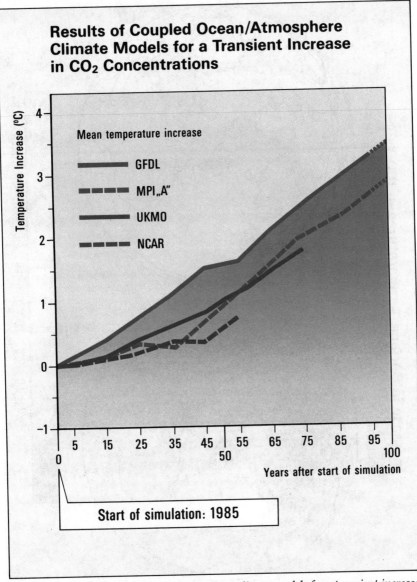

Fig. 3.4: Results of coupled ocean/atmosphere climate models for a transient increase in CO_2 concentrations over a maximum period of 100 years (see text).
Start of the simulation: 1985
Mean temperature rise (°C)
(from: Cubasch, 1992)

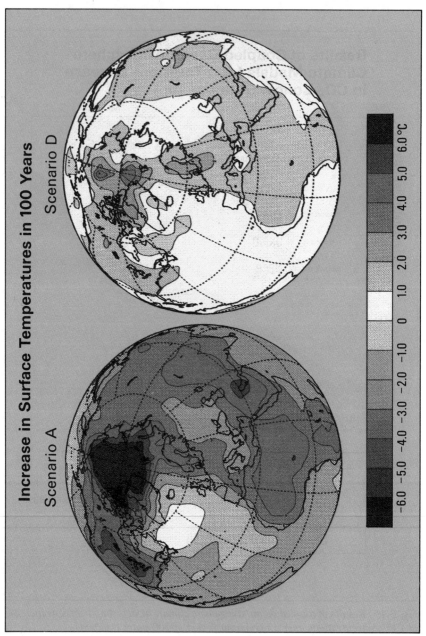

Fig. 3.5: Increase in atmospheric surface temperatures (by the year 2085) for IPCC scenarios A and D.
Source: MPI and DKRZ, Hamburg

- Initially, warming will be more pronounced in the tropics than at higher latitudes. However, the higher latitudes will catch up as warming progresses. When atmospheric CO_2 concentrations will have doubled relative to pre-industrial levels, warming will be most pronounced at northern high latitudes.
- Due to global warming and the resulting increase in surface water evaporation, there will be a general trend towards increasing precipitation. This will mainly be true for the higher latitudes of both hemispheres, and for the northern mid-latitudes in winter.
- In summer, however, there will be a general decline in precipitation above land surfaces, which will lead to a substantial reduction of soil moisture with adverse effects on plant growth.

Furthermore, the simulation runs carried out with the Hamburg climate model predicted that, at the time when double the equivalent CO_2 concentration is reached, the Arctic ice sheet will have considerably contracted in size. Similar results are obtained by a simple extrapolation of the trends that have already been observed (increasing atmospheric water vapour concentrations and more pronounced warming at tropical latitudes, more intensive general circulation, and hence, increasing poleward transport of atmospheric heat) (12).

Even if it was possible to stabilise the atmospheric concentrations of radiatively active trace substances at current levels, atmospheric surface temperatures would continue to rise because of the time lag effect caused by the high heat storage capacity of the oceans. Thus, a new equilibrium would only be reached in 20 to 30 years' time.

3.3   Rise of Sea Level

The sea level is subject to short-term and regional variations which depend on atmospheric pressure, wind and tidal conditions. The mean sea level can be calculated by averaging the varying sea levels observed over time. However, the mean sea level is not constant in the long term. In fact, it has varied considerably in the more recent history of the Earth: in a matter of 10,000 years – between the climax phase of the last glacial period (about 18,000 years ago) and the transition to the subsequent interglacial period – it rose by about 120 meters. This substantial rise was due to the melting of large glaciers and inland ice areas in the Northern Hemisphere when temperatures increased by 3 to 4 °C. Today, only a small fraction of the land surface in the Northern Hemisphere is still covered by ice. For this reason, the response of the sea level to increasing global temperatures will be much less drastic. The extent of the sea level rise to be expected can be assessed on the basis of sea level observations which go back about 100 years. In this period of time, during which global temperatures increased by about 0.6 °C, the sea level rose by about 1 to 2 millimeters per year. On the basis of numerous empirical studies, the following parameters can be described as key factors for changes in sea level:

- thermal expansion of sea water,
- melting of mountain glaciers,
- melting of smaller inland ice caps (e.g. in Greenland), and increase in the Antarctic ice sheet.

The sea level is not affected, however, by melting sea ice. In the 100-year period under review, the very slow process of crustal deformation does not have any major impact on the sea level either. The rise of sea level observed over the past 100 years has been essentially due the first two factors mentioned, whereas the melting of the Greenland ice sheet has had a relatively minor impact (see Table 3.1). With increasing temperatures, the ice sheet on the Antarctic continent has probably grown, which tends to suggest a negative feedback effect with regard to the rise of sea level (13).

Based on the data collected – which show a clear relationship between the increase in mean global temperatures and the sea level – and in conjunction with climate model predictions, it is possible to estimate the future trend in sea level. In a first step, the calculations made had to be limited to roughly estimating the effects of the temperature trends (predicted by non-coupled climate models) on the ice sheets and on ocean expansion. Based on IPCC scenario A (CO_2 doubling by the year 2050), the models predicted a rise of sea level by between 30 and 50 cm by the year 2050, and by between 70 and 100 cm by the year 2100. Table 3.2 shows the

Table 3.1: *Various Factors Affecting the Sea Level Rise in the Past 100 Years (centimeters)*
(Oerlemans, 1990)

	Low	Best estimate	High
Thermal expansion	2	4	6
Glaciers / small ice caps	1.5	4	7
Greeland ice sheet	1	2.5	4
Antarctic ice sheet	−5	0	5
Total	−0.5	10.5	22

Table 3.2: *Various Factors Affecting the Predicted Sea Level Rise 1985-2030 in Accordance with IPCC Scenario "Business as Usual" (centimeters) (Oerlemans, 1990)*

	Thermal expansion	Mountain glaciers	Greenland	Antarctica	Total
High	14.9	10.3	3.7	0.0	28.9
Best estimate	10.1	7.0	1.8	−0.6	18.3
Low	6.8	2.3	0.5	−0.8	8.7

respective effects of the factors mentioned earlier. The possibility of the western Antarctic ice sheet (which is anchored below the ocean surface) breaking apart, as predicted by some models, was not included in the calculation because there is no evidence suggesting that this might happen in the course of the next 100 years. However, it must be borne in mind as a major potential threat for subsequent centuries. If the western Antarctic ice sheet melts, this might lead to a rise of sea level by up to 40 cm over a period of 200 years, and by another 30 cm over a period of 300 years (14). During the Eem interglacial period (125,000 years ago), the melting of the western Antarctic shelf ice led to a sea level rise by about 6 meters. At the time, the mean global temperature was 2 °C above the pre-industrial level.

Recent calculations, based on coupled ocean/atmosphere models, suggest that the sea level will rise by between 6 and 25 cm over the next 100 years. What is also striking is that the annual rates at which the sea level will rise will accelerate in the course of the next century. However, these predictions are only based on the thermal expansion of the ocean water so that the IPCC predictions are more or less confirmed. Another important point to be borne in mind for both scenarios is that no equilibrium is reached between temperature increases and sea level rise in the period under review. Instead, both scenarios suggest that the upward trend can be expected to continue even after the year 2100. However, a more precise calculation would be scientifically untenable because of the uncertainty of the data involved.

If the sea level rises by about 50 cm, this will constitute a serious threat for millions of people, and it will have considerable ecological and socio-economic repercussions such as:

- flooding of lowland plains and wetlands near coastlines,
- erosion of coastlines,
- increase in storm tides,
- salinisation of estuaries, deltas and groundwater resources, as well as other adverse effects on water quality,
- changes in tidal rise,
- changes in sedimentation,
- decrease in easily accessible groundwater beds.

If the sea level rises by only a few decimeters, a large number of coastal plains – many of them densely populated – will be flooded. Areas that are particularly at risk include the estuaries of the rivers Nile, Ganges, Yangtse, Mekong, Irriwaddy, Indus, Niger, Parana, Amazon, Mississippi, and Po, as well as various Pacific island states such as Kiribati, Takelau, Tuvalu, and the Maldive Islands. Large land areas of these island states, which are just a few meters above the current sea level, are at risk of becoming uninhabitable because of the predicted changes. However, the United States (land loss caused by sea level rise of 1 meter is estimated at about 20,000 square kilometers) and Europe will also be directly affected if the sea level rises (see Fig. 3.6). Overall, it is assumed that about 350,000 kilometers of coastline, roughly 6,400 kilometers of urban coastline, as well as 10,700 kilometers of tourist sand beaches and 1,800 square kilometers of harbour and port areas will have to be protected from the imminent threat of a rising sea level. The areas just mentioned only cover coastal regions with population densities of more than 10 inhabitants per square kilometer. For many countries, it will be virtually impossible to pay for the costs which this would require. According to preliminary estimates, the annual costs incurred by the Pacific island states, for instance, just for protective measures would amount to between 5 and 34 percent of their gross national products. However, some African (Gambia, Liberia, Mozambique, etc.) and Latin American countries (Guyana, Surinam, Belize, etc.) would encounter the same difficulties.

In addition to permanent flooding, a rise of sea level will increase the frequency and intensity of large-scale flood disasters. However, such disasters will be due not only to a higher sea level but also to the destruction of natural barriers such as coral reefs, offshore sand bars, lagoons, etc., and to reduced inland drainage by rivers and canals. This means that rivers will also break their banks more frequently, causing large-scale floods in countries such as Bangladesh, China, the southeastern part of the United States and India, which may be further amplified by changes in the moisture regime (e.g. shifts in monsoons or snowmelts).

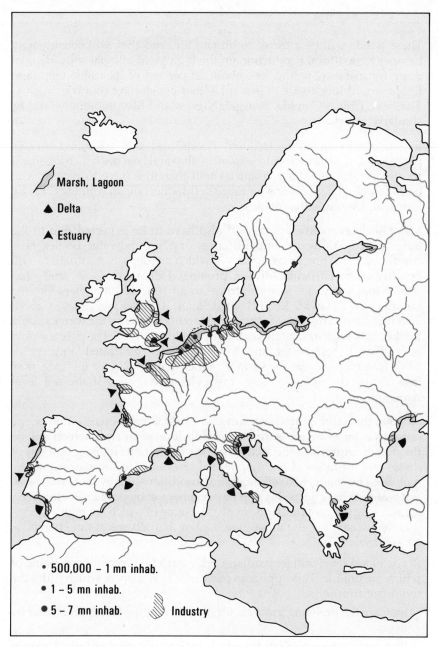

Fig. 3.6:   *European coastal regions jeopardised by a rise in sea level and by salt water intruding into estuaries and groundwater bodies*
Source: European Workshop on Interrelated Bioclimate and Land Use Change

The following legend appears within the figure:

- Marsh, Lagoon
- ▲ Delta
- ▲ Estuary
- • 500,000 – 1 mn inhab.
- • 1 – 5 mn inhab.
- • 5 – 7 mn inhab.
- Industry

These floods will be a threat to human life, and they will considerably hamper agricultural production on the high-yield alluvial soils. Bangladesh, for instance, would lose about 20 percent of its arable land, and Egypt would lose about 15 percent. Other developing countries such as Thailand, China, Gambia, Senegal, Nigeria and Mozambique would be similarly at risk.

In some regions, more frequent floods and the associated erosive processes at coastlines would jeopardise the sand beaches which are major tourist attractions. Many countries will therefore have to reckon with considerable repercussions on tourism (Mediterranean countries, Brazil, Portugal, United States, etc.).

Major socio-economic effects will also have to be expected due to the intrusion of salt water into estuaries and groundwater bodies near coastlines. Estuarine areas – many of which are densely populated – will be affected in particular during prolonged dry periods. A study has shown that salt water would intrude about 10 to 20 kilometers into the mouth of the Delaware River (United States) if the sea level rises by about 50 centimeters. This would have considerable effects on the water supply for the millions of inhabitants of the city of Philadelphia. The effects would be similar if salt water and brackish water infiltrated aquifers or fresh-water lenses near the surface. Some Pacific atolls, for instance, may lose about 50 percent of their fresh-water reservoirs if the sea level rises.

Another threat for groundwater and surface water resources, whose scope cannot yet be assessed, is due to landfills located in areas which will be flooded in future, and the accumulation of pollutants in the sediments of deltas and estuaries of highly polluted rivers. Toxic substances may be mobilised by changes in sedimentation conditions and by the intrusion of salt water. What effects this will have cannot yet be predicted. However, considering the contaminants involved – some of which are highly toxic – it is safe to say that the threat potential of this "chemical time bomb" is considerable (15).

A rise of sea level will jeopardise a wide variety of ecosystems, some of which are unique. This applies in particular to wetlands, which fulfill the following functions:

- they are the breeding grounds for one-third of the fish species used by man;

- they offer unique habitats for a wide variety of animal and plant species (e.g. tidal flats, mangroves), and

- they are natural barriers which offer protection against floods.

While it is possible that the wetlands may move inland, the maximum migration rate of wetlands which are not hampered by barriers could offset a sea level rise of no more than 1 cm per year, which will be reached by the end of the next century. What effects the poleward migration of these ecosystems will have is still uncertain. Generally speaking, however, it will not be possible for ecosystems located in inshore wetlands to keep pace with the encroachment of the oceans. Up to two-thirds of the wetlands in the United States, for instance, are expected to be lost, if the sea level rises by about 1 meter and if all the densely populated coastal regions have to be protected by appropriate structures (13). Areas with low tidal ranges (e.g. the coastlines of the Mediterranean and the Black Sea, and the Gulf of Mexico) would be affected as severely. About half of the roughly 750,000 square kilometers of wetlands worldwide, and about half of the 165,000 square kilometers of mangroves, are found in the following countries: Mexico, Brazil, Argentina, Cuba, Indonesia, Papua New Guinea, Viet Nam, and Malaysia. About 88 percent of these areas have population densities of more than 10 inhabitants per square kilometer, and hence, have to be protected. The destruction of these ecologically important areas can already be described as "inevitable". As much as 5 to 10 percent of the wetland area losses would be directly due to the construction of protective installations.

The global diversity of species will be reduced by the destruction of wetlands and dune areas, and by the bleaching of coral reefs. The effects of this development are already noticeable today (16). In addition, there is a risk that there may be severe repercussions for the fishery industry as well (see Chapter 3.4.2 Marine ecosystems).

3.4   Effects on Natural Ecosystems

The biosphere plays a key role in the hydrological cycle, the nutrient cycle and the carbon cycle, and it is subject to complex interactions with the soils and the atmosphere. The changes to be expected with regard to the climate and the chemical composition of the atmosphere will have a major impact, therefore, on the spatial distribution and composition of natural biotic communities. Climate model predictions suggest that many ecosystems will not be able to adjust to the rapidly changing conditions. This will have both ecological and dramatic socio-economic consequences.

3.4.1 Terrestrial ecosystems

About one-third of the Earth's land surface is occupied by ecosystems which are either not used at all by man, or only extensively so. This includes natural forests as well as a variety of highly different forms of landscape, e.g. mountainous ecosystems, savannah areas, deserts, etc. (17). Increasing atmospheric CO_2 concentrations and shifting climatic zones affect the equilibrium between natural biotic communities and their local living conditions – an equilibrium which has taken a long time to develop. From today's perspective, it is hardly possible to predict the specific effects which this will have for the following reasons:

- While it is true that ecosystems have a buffering capacity which enables them to survive extreme weather conditions, this buffering capacity will be exhausted and will collapse if extreme weather events persist or occur in rapid sequence.
- Natural biotic communities survive by a complex network of interactions among the living organisms themselves, and between the organisms and their physical and chemical environmental conditions.
- By and large, there is a lack of synergistic models and experiments which would make it possible to study the effects of increasing CO_2 concentrations and climate change in combination with changes in other environmental parameters (e.g. increasing UV-B radiation, near-surface ozone concentrations, etc.).

Nonetheless, the two factors which are discussed below seem to be crucial for the future development of terrestrial ecosystems.

3.4.1.1 *Net primary production and storage of carbon in the biosphere*

Terrestrial plants store about 60 Gt C per year in newly formed biomass. In the same period of time, the carbon contained in dead biomass amounts to between 40 and 50 Gt C. The global carbon volume stored in biotic waste totals about 60 Gt C (7). All in all, this suggests an even carbon balance between the atmosphere and the biosphere. This even balance is perturbed, however, by about 6 to 7 Gt C annually released into the atmosphere due to the combustion of fossil fuels, and by about 1 to 2 Gt C released due to tropical deforestation. The largest part of these additional carbon emissions remains in the atmosphere (about 3.5 to 4.0 Gt C), whereas the fate of the remainder is controversial. While Tans et al. (1990) estimate the amount of carbon which is annually absorbed by the oceans at between 0.5 and 1.0 Gt C, the IPCC assumes that the oceans are capable of storing 2.0 ± 0.8 Gt C per year. The carbon stored in terrestrial biomass is estimated to be between 1.6 and 4.0 Gt C per annum (18).

If one compares the carbon fluxes between the atmosphere, the oceans and the biosphere between 1860 and 1980, based on the results of the "Osnabrück Biosphere Model", it is striking that there was a slight increase in annual net primary production (NPP) of biomass, and that an additional 73 Gt C was stored in biomass due to the "CO_2 fertilising effect" (see Table 3.3). For this reason – despite progressing tropical deforestation, involving the release of between 1 and 2 Gt C per year – the terrestrial biomass is still regarded as a carbon sink which will continue to absorb part of the atmospheric CO_2, thereby mitigating climate change. This applies in particular to the northern mid-latitudes.

Numerous experiments have also shown that there is a positive feedback between atmospheric CO_2 concentrations and the net primary production of various plants. In fact, at a CO_2 level of 600 ppm, respiratory losses were found to be reduced by up to 50 percent, and biomass production increased by up to 30 percent. In addition, the plants' water utilisation efficiency increased considerably. However, the effects observed were by no means clear; instead, they depended on the supply of water, light and nutrients, and on the respective chemical carbon binding process in the plants. In this context, a distinction must be made between C3 and C4 plants. The former first of all bind carbon to a sugar which contains five C atoms. The resulting compound with 6 C atoms then breaks up into two chains with three C atoms each (C3). On the other hand, C4 plants first of all bind CO_2 to a C3 compound. The C4 unit which results is then subject to further reactions.

Experiments carried out with a one-year C3 plant (rush) in the wetlands of the American East Coast showed that net primary production continued to increase in the presence of a CO_2 concentration of 700 ppm. However, this effect was hardly noticeable when the same experiment was carried out with a C4 plant. In this direct competition, therefore, the C4 plant was clearly inferior. However, these results cannot be simply applied to other regions because the supply of water and of nutrients was better than average in the area where the experiments were carried out (13).

In a similar experiment carried out in the tundra, net primary production increased much less rapidly. Over time, the curve reflecting the rate of increase became much flatter. In this case, the CO_2 fertilising effect may have been more than offset by the rate of degradation of dead organic matter, which increases with increasing temperatures, so that this would lead to a net CO_2 source (13).

Table 3.3: *Annual and Accumulation Carbon Fluxes in the Terrestrial Biomass and the Oceans — Global Trends between 1860 and 1980, Based on Results of the "Osnabrück Biosphere Model"[1] (Esser, 1989)*

Year	Carbon fluxes							
	Accumulation carbon fluxes (since 1860)				Annual carbon fluxes			
	Fossil fuels	Oceans	Clearings	CO_2-fertilising effect	Net primary production	Litter	Soil organic matter	Burnt
(1)	(2)	(3)	(4)	(5)	(6)	(7)	(8)	(9)
1860	− 0	0	− 0	0	44	−33	−11	−0.0
1870	− 1	1	− 7	2	44	−33	−11	−0.3
1880	− 3	3	−15	5	44	−34	−11	−0.3
1890	− 6	4	−22	8	44	−33	−11	−0.1
1900	− 10	8	−30	12	44	−34	−11	−0.3
1910	− 17	12	−37	15	44	−34	−11	−0.3
1920	− 26	17	−44	19	44	−34	−11	−0.2
1930	− 36	23	−54	25	44	−34	−11	−0.2
1940	− 47	30	−63	31	44	−34	−11	−0.2
1950	− 61	37	−73	38	45	−34	−11	−0.2
1960	− 82	47	−81	47	45	−34	−11	−0.3
1970	−115	59	−89	58	45	−33	−11	−0.2
1980	−163	76	−96	73	46	−34	−11	−0.1

[1] The model does not take into account the climate change which occurred during the period under review.

The reaction patterns observed in the Mexican rain forest were yet again different. Here, higher CO_2 concentrations produced an increase in net primary production only for some C3 tree species, while in other C3 trees the opposite effect occurred. The results seem to have been particularly influenced by the limited incidence of light (20).

Generally speaking, one should be cautious in assessing the validity of these experimental findings because most of these experiments were devoted exclusively to studying the effect of increasing CO_2 concentrations. In reality, however, ecosystems are exposed to a variety of overlapping changes such as increasing temperatures, changing precipitation patterns, increasing UV-B radiation, etc. In addition, there is growing evidence suggesting that net primary production can only increase if, at the same time, the supply of water, light and nutrients is guaranteed over the entire vegetation period. According to climate model predictions, however, this will be true for only a few regions of the Earth. In fact, current estimates suggest that these regions will be limited to the northern latitudes and parts of the mid-latitudes (see 3.6 Agriculture). In the Mediterranean regions, as well as in the tropics and subtropics, ecosystems can be expected to be exposed predominantly to adverse effects.

What impact the CO_2 fertilising effect will have, to a large extent will also depend on the rate at which organic matter is degraded in the soil. Overall, the amount of carbon stored in soils is much greater (about 1,500 Gt C) than the amount of carbon stored in living biomass. Depending on the amount of water available, as well as the chemical composition of litter and various soil characteristics, the rate of degradation increases with increasing temperatures. As the tundra example has shown, the additional amount of CO_2 released can surpass the increase in biomass caused by higher atmospheric CO_2 concentrations. There is a risk that the global volume of carbon stored in living and dead biomass may also decrease. In this process, considerable carbon emissions would be added to the emissions due to the combustion of fossil fuels, which might lead to a drastic increase in the greenhouse effect.

In addition, recent studies suggest that an increase in net primary production will have an impact on nutrient absorption. The nitrogen content of leaves, for instance, was found to decrease if biomass production increases. The effect which this would have on plant-eating insects would be that they would have to consume more leaf material in order to cover their protein demand (20).

It seems questionable whether there will actually be a CO_2 fertilising effect. Only synergistic experiments and models could provide conclusive evidence. For this purpose, however, it is necessary to improve our understanding of carbon fluxes within the ecosystems, and between the natural biotic communities and the atmosphere. In addition, precise predictions about regional climate changes to be expected would have to be available, taking into account the annual variability of temperatures and precipitation.

3.4.1.2   Shifts of vegetation zones and changes in species composition

Information about vegetation zone shifts due to global climate change can be obtained from an evaluation of palaeoclimatic data and from our knowledge about the vulnerability of natural ecosystems.

In the Earth's recent history, there have been several shifts of vegetation zones due to climate change. During the last interglacial period (70,000 to 10,000 years ago), for instance, most of Europe was covered by tundra vegetation. As temperatures increased, this vegetation was once again replaced by forests. Such shifts occurred without any human interventions in natural cycles. Nevertheless, many plant species were unable to adjust to the changes in climatic conditions and became extinct. The fact that, when compared to other continents, Europe has relatively few tree species is due to the many glacial periods alternating with interglacial periods.

However, these natural shifts are not comparable with the man-made changes which will occur in future. It seems doubtful whether the ecosystems will be able to respond sufficiently fast to the man-made increase in atmospheric CO_2 concentrations and to the climate change expected. If the warming rate proves to be between 2° and 5°C, as predicted, the next century will see the highest temperatures of the past 200,000 years. The rapidity of this climate change constitutes a threat for a variety of plant species. It is assumed that for each degree Celsius by which the temperature will rise, the vegetation zones will make a poleward move of between 200 and 300 kilometers. It can be safely assumed that seeds of trees travel a maximum of 100 to 200 meters before they reach the ground, and that the trees growing from these seeds take years or decades before they produce new seeds. For this reason, it is impossible for a tree species to increase its distribution area by several hundred kilometers in one century. The threat which natural ecosystems are exposed to is aggravated by the fact that some of them have already been suffering from ecological stress due to human activities (groundwater depletion, air pollution, soil acidification, overgrazing, local climate change, etc.). The increase in wind velocities expected in future also represents a particularly serious threat. If there is an increase in the frequency and intensity of catastrophic storm events (low-pressure systems with gale-force winds, tropical cyclones), this will also do major damage to natural ecosystems.

Generally speaking, terrestrial ecosystems will be confronted with two threats: on the one hand, the global increase in CO_2 concentrations, and on the other hand, the associated regional climate change. Weighing predominantly positive effects (CO_2 fertilisation) against predominantly negative effects (due to climate change) seems to be a futile exercise in the case of natural ecosystems, since any short-term change in environmental parameters will upset an ecosystem's natural equilibrium which has taken a long time to develop. Only certain plants would benefit from the CO_2 fertilising effect, for instance, and these plants would be able to spread at the expense of others. Such a change in the competitive situation within a natural biotic community may have a destabilising effect on the ecosystems concerned.

In the process of adjusting to climate change, ecosystems will certainly migrate. However, there is general agreement that ecosystems will not migrate as a whole, but that each species will develop its own response pattern. Some species will benefit in relative terms, while others will disappear. It is not yet possible to predict the effects of this selection pressure. However, there are fears that pathogens and pests may spread rapidly.

It is also very difficult to predict regional vegetation shifts. Neither an evaluation of palaeoclimatic data nor climate modelling has so far permitted predictions of regional changes in climatic parameters. In addition, the data available are limited to predictions of changes in mean temperature and precipitation. In reality, however, ecosystems are also affected both by the annual variability of specific climate factors and by extreme events (e. g. droughts, sudden frost episodes, etc.). Accordingly, their specific natural elasticity varies widely. Generally speaking, the relatively unstable ecosystems in semi-arid, arid or cold regions seem to be particularly at risk. A slight change in the dry periods of savannah areas, for instance, can lead to severe degradation. For alpine ecosystems, there is also a risk of irreversible damage if temperature and precipitation patterns change (21).

All in all, shifts of natural ecosystems may bring about a decline in global species diversity. Regions with high proportions of cultivated land (e.g. Central Europe) – and correspondingly limited scope for compensation – seem to be particularly at risk. It is not yet possible to predict the effects of such a development (16).

3.4.1.3 Socio-economic effects

If natural and quasi-natural ecosystems are impaired, this will have major socio-economic consequences, in particular in the developing countries where most people are directly dependent on intact natural ecosystems. Not only do they provide firewood; they are also a source of building material, food and drugs. In addition, nomadic tribes use them as grazing areas for the extensive type of cattle farming they practise. Even minor shifts of precipitation patterns might lead to shifts in species composition and increasing degradation of ecosystems in semi-arid areas, which are at risk anyway. This would deprive many people of the prerequisites to their survival (see 3.6 Agriculture).

However, industrialised societies also make use of natural and quasi-natural ecosystems. Most of these natural ecosystems are of high aesthetic value and are mainly used for recreational purposes. This function of the ecosystems will be jeopardised by future climate change. Any shifts in species composition, for instance, might severely alter the character of nature parks which are important tourist destinations. This also applies to regions outside the industrialised nations, which are highly dependent on tourism.

In addition, intact natural and quasi-natural ecosystems also offer indirect benefits: they mitigate extreme weather events, offer protection against avalanches, prevent wind and water erosion, and act as sinks for a large number of trace substances. If these benefits were lost, this would have a major impact on the industrialised nations as well (e. g. higher frequency of avalanches, mud flows and landslides in mountainous regions).

3.4.2 Marine ecosystems

3.4.2.1 Threat potential

Marine organisms absorb about 40 Gt C per year. Roughly 2.0 ± 0.8 Gt C remains in living algae whose population is characterised by highly dynamic changes.

In the oceans, primary biomass production is mainly controlled by the light and nutrient conditions prevailing, while the temperature plays a much less important role. About 45 percent of the marine biomass is found at high latitudes, another 20 percent in coastal shelf regions (13). Nutrient supply depends primarily on the presence of deep-sea water welling up. This process, which is coupled with the general circulation of the oceans, is controlled by climatic factors (temperature and wind). Hence, climate change will be of great importance for marine ecosystems.

The relationship between the climate and ocean circulation is reflected in the climate models, and it has also been confirmed by palaeoclimatic studies. Since the last glacial period (70,000 to 10,000 years ago), for instance, ocean circulation has substantially decreased, which has led to a decline in productivity, in particular at higher latitudes. For this reason, the climate change predicted for the future can be expected to bring about distinct shifts in the spatial distribution and the structure of marine ecosystems.

The increase in ocean surface temperatures, which is already noticeable, has led to a poleward migration of various marine biocenoses. In future, this trend will accelerate. Like the species in terrestrial ecosystems, not all marine species will be equally successful in adjusting to changes in their environment, so that the species composition can be expected to change (13).

The expected decline in ocean circulation will have a particularly severe impact. The ecological equilibrium of areas which, today, are high in nutrient content and productivity will be severely disturbed. This is illustrated by the example of the El Niño effect off the western coast of South America which, in irregular intervals, brings death to numerous marine organisms. Such anomalies, which might occur more frequently in the future, will cause not only ecological but also severe socio-economic effects (13).

The decline in ocean glaciation will also have a major impact on marine ecosystems, affecting both the algae growing at the ice boundaries and the larger mammals living there. While the prolonged growth period will not necessarily reduce productivity, substantial structural changes are likely to occur in the energy and substance fluxes between ecosystems at the boundary between ocean water and ice. Negative feedbacks, for instance, can be expected with regard to the high algae productivity in this area. The algae, in turn, are the main source of food for the higher forms of life.

Synergistic effects also play a role for marine ecosystems. The ecological disruptions caused by overfishing, for instance, will have an impact on the future composition of species under changing conditions. In addition, higher temperatures might amplify the effects of increasing ocean pollution. The expected increase in UV-B radiation intensity will also have adverse effects on the productivity and the ability of marine ecosystems to adjust to changing conditions. On the one hand, this might lead to a reduction of the sink function of the oceans and a corresponding positive feedback on the greenhouse effect; on the other hand, higher UV-B radiation intensity at higher latitudes will jeopardise important ecosystems in coastal areas and at ice boundaries. These ecosystems serve as breeding grounds for a variety of fish species, and hence, are of particular importance for the reproduction rates of these species. There is still a considerable need for research aimed at identifying the consequences of such synergistic effects.

3.4.2.2 Socio-economic effects

It can be assumed that climate change will have an adverse impact on the species composition and the productivity of marine ecosystems, and that it will have severe effects on fishery and downstream industries. While certain fish species can be expected to benefit from the predicted changes and will spread at the expense of other species, overall this development will constitute a massive threat for fishery, in particular in areas which are currently characterised by strong circulation and high productivity. The severity of the climatically induced changes is illustrated by the major losses suffered by Peru's fishery industry in connection with the El Niño effect. The risk that such phenomena may occur is particularly high for coastline countries which are situated along ocean zones with rapidly upwelling high-nutrient deep-sea water. Many of these countries will not be able to compensate for the adverse economic effects of such phenomena (e. g. Namibia, Mauritania, Peru, Somalia) (13).

3.5 Effects on Forestry

About one-third of the Earth's land surface is covered by forests and woodlands (cf. Table 3.4 and Table 3.5). Mankind uses a large part of these forms of vegetation in various ways. In this context, there is no clear-cut dividing line between natural and quasi-natural forest ecosystems on the one hand, and intensively managed forests on the other hand. It is difficult, therefore, to offer a precise definition of what managed forests are. Following the IPCC, the comments below refer to forests which are systematically used by man. The focus will be on forests which are subject to methodical management.

Because of the longevity of their tree populations, forest ecosystems do not easily adjust to changes in ecological conditions. For this reason, they will be particularly affected by the expected climate change. Rising temperatures, for instance, will lead to an increase in evapotranspiration which can only be compensated for – although to a limited extent only – if precipitation frequency and intensity increases at the same time. Further-more, the respiration rate of trees will increase in response to higher temperatures. This will reduce the rate of growth in forests which have already reached their maximum net primary production. In areas, however, where the temperature is a limiting growth factor, net primary production will increase. In addition, a warmer climate will change the competitive situation prevailing in forest ecosystems, and it will promote the proliferation of pests and diseases. This will apply in particular to semi-arid regions which already suffer from water stress.

Furthermore, single-species managed forests are more at risk than mixed forests. Another threat for forestry emanates from the expected increase in the frequency of extreme weather events. This includes not only storms

Table 3.4: Forest Area Proportions of Total Land Area, 1980 (IPCC WG II, 1990)

Region	Total land area (million ha)	Forest land area (million ha)	Forest area proportion of total land in the region (percent)	Forest area proportion of total world forests (percent)	Forest land area per inhabitant (ha/person)
World total	13,075	4,094	31.3	100.0	0.9
Developed regions ...	5,485	1,829	33.3	44.7	1.6
North America	1,835	611	33.3	14.9	2.4
Western Europe	373	126	33.8	3.1	0.3
Eastern Europe	100	29	29.0	0.7	0.3
USSR	2,227	920	41.3	22.5	3.5
Japan	37	25	67.6	0.6	0.2
Other*)	913	118	12.9	2.9	2.3
Developing regions ..	7,591	2,264	29.0	55.3	0.7
Africa	2,331	642	27.5	15.7	1.7
Near East	1,192	98	8.2	2.4	0.5
China	931	116	12.5	2.8	0.1
Other Asia/Pacific ...	1,028	356	34.6	8.7	0.3
Latin America	2,020	1,015	50.2	24.8	2.8
Other **)	88	37	42.0	0.9	7.2

*) Australia, Israel, New Zealand, South Africa
**) Pacific islands and Greenland

but also prolonged dry periods and isolated frost episodes in an otherwise milder climate. Higher mean temperature would also increase the susceptibility of mid-latitude summer-green forests to frost because leaf shed – which is a prerequisite to overwintering – would be deferred till the winter months. Another important point will be more frequent fires which will aggravate the selection pressure and change the fluxes of substances between the biosphere and the atmosphere.

Based on the current status of knowledge, it seems questionable whether the so-called CO_2 fertilising effect will compensate – at least to some extent – for the adverse effects outlined above. In field trials, it has not been possible to demonstrate that the net primary production of forests increases in response to higher atmospheric CO_2 concentrations. The

Table 3.5: Forest Resources and Forest Use in Major Forestry Countries (IPCC WG II, 1990)

	Indonesia	China	India	Brazil	Kenya
Forest land (million ha) .	122	135	67	565	3.7
Productive forest land (million ha)	45	122	45	350	1.1
Managed forest (thousand ha)	1,918	12,733	2,062	3,855	181

	Zambia	Finland	New Zealand	Chile
Forest land (million ha) .	29.5	23.3	10.6	15.5
Productive forest land (million ha)	4.1	18.2	2.8	4.7
Managed forest (thousand ha)	38	145	1,200	817

	Canada	USA	Austria	Federal Republic of Germany
Forest land (million ha) .	452	265	3.2	7.3
Productive forest land (million ha)	244	210	3.0	7.3
Managed forest (thousand ha)	450	917	25	70

increases in biomass growth rates in European forests, found by FAO, are probably due to the substantial input of nitrogen from the air (22).

The magnitude of the effects described above will vary widely from region to region. It can be assumed that there will be a shift of vegetation zones. In fact, for each degree Celsius of temperature rise, the vegetation zones can be expected to move poleward by between 200 and 300 kilometers (13). If temperatures rise to the point predicted for a doubling of CO_2 concentrations, the boreal forest zone, for instance, will move to where the tundra is today, and it will lose about 40 percent of its size in the process. The surface area of the subtropical forests could be expected to decrease by about 20 percent, while tropical forest areas would probably grow by about 30 percent. The question as to whether forests can actually adjust to such a change in climatic and ecological conditions, will mainly depend on their maximum migration rates. Although no studies have yet been made on specific species, it is generally assumed that the trees will usually not be able to expand their distribution areas fast enough, and hence, they will be more and more "out of sync" with their environment. Their migration will be hampered by two obstacles: first of all, areas used as farmland which will act as a barrier; and secondly, insufficient quality of soils which have evolved under specific climatic conditions over a period of thousands of years. The forest areas which are subject to ecological stress can be expected to increase drastically in the next few decades. In the United States, forest areas are expected to decline in the dry central and western parts of the country in about 30 years' time, in the mid-west in about 30 to 60 years, and in the southeast in roughly 60 to 70 years' time (13). In Australia, the distribution area of Pinus radiata and Eucalyptus regnans might disappear altogether. In addition, negative synergistic effects are to be expected in many regions of the Earth. Higher ozone surface concentrations, for instance, in the vicinity of industrial agglomerations will considerably exacerbate the climate stress. Large-scale acidification of forest soils – a phenomenon which is particularly common in Europe – will also have a similar effect. In those parts of the tropics where dry periods predominate vis-à-vis rainy periods, the climatic stress will be joined by stress due to overutilisation, which is already dramatically felt today. In addition, relatively minor changes in precipitation patterns will have severe consequences for ecosystems in those regions. Forests in mountainous and alpine vegetation zones are also subject to a considerable risk. While there will be an overall rise of the alpine tree line because of the increase in temperatures, the unstable ecosystems in this vegetation zone will respond sensitively to any perturbation, so that even minor departures from today's climate may cause considerable damage.

125

The ecological changes described above will have a direct impact on the utility value of the forests. While it is possible to influence the shifts of forest ecosystems by means of forest management measures (e.g. increasing forest species diversity, cultivating resistant tree species, or shortening felling cycles), there can be no doubt that these ecological changes can be expected to have severe repercussions on forestry. Harvest times will be shorter in the boreal zone, for instance, where logging is carried out during winter when the soil is frozen, and hence, fit to carry vehicles. Increasing ecological stress will reduce the survival rate of newly planted young trees, and it will generally require more intensive management. Once again, the severity of the impact will vary from region to region. On the whole, boreal forests will suffer much less damage than forests in arid and semi-arid regions and in mountainous areas. This means that the socio-economic effects will tend to be positive for Canada's forestry sector, while the effects in the United States will tend to be negative.

The extent to which forestry will suffer from the effects of the changes described above will depend not only on the specific ecological conditions but also on the prevailing infrastructure. A well-developed infrastructure will facilitate silvicultural countermeasures. In this context, it should be borne in mind that, if forests migrate, it will be necessary to build up the infrastructure required in the new distribution areas. This will involve substantial costs.

3.6   Effects on Agriculture

By now, there is sufficient evidence which demonstrates that agriculture will be affected in various ways by the climate change to be expected. Changes in climate parameters (temperatures, precipitation, clouds) and in the chemical composition of the atmosphere will have a major impact on food production. Shifts of climatic belts will call for substantial changes in farming methods. Attention will also have to be paid to the predicted rise of sea level, because floods will destroy valuable cultivated areas (see Chapter 3.3).

The two key factors determining the level of agricultural yields are the distribution of precipitation and soil moisture. Temperatures also have a major impact; the important point, however, is not so much the average temperature increase but the maximum and minimum temperatures reached. Predictions of current climate models with regard to these factors are of poor quality and lack precision. Although some progress has been made in recent years, the question as to how precipitation and temperatures will change at regional level is still open to scientific debate. For this reason, it has not been possible yet to answer the question of whether global food production will increase or decrease in response to the expected climate change.

However, there is agreement about the fact that the impact of climate change will be unevenly distributed. Certain regions will suffer considerably from the higher temperatures predicted, while other regions will be able to increase their production volumes. The direct socio-economic effects of changing production conditions will be particularly severe in the field of agriculture, especially in the developing countries which have no technical or financial scope for adjustment.

All these developments must be seen against the background of the problems which will be caused by rapid world population growth even if there were no climate change. In fact, the world population will grow from currently 5 billion people to 8.5 billion by the year 2025. Bearing in mind that many regions of the Earth already suffer from insufficient food supply, agricultural production would have to grow by at least 75 percent over the next 30 years, or by 2.5 percent annually (23). Between 1960 and 1990, annual growth rates ranged between 2 and 3 percent, but then began to decline in 1991 (24). Agriculture will have to meet considerable requirements, not only with regard to food production, but also in terms of the provision of land, fresh water and fuel.

3.6.1 Direct physiological effects of CO_2, increasing UV-B radiation and air pollutants on plants, soils and animals

Plant species can be subdivided into two major groups which differ in the biochemical processes used to fix CO_2 during photosynthesis. C3 plants bind CO_2 to a sugar which contains five C atoms. The resulting compound consisting of 6 C atoms then breaks up into two sugars with three C atoms each (C3). On the other hand, C4 plants first of all bind CO_2 to a C3 compound. The CO_2 is temporarily stored in the resulting C4 compound before it is converted into a more efficient form for photosynthesis.

In a complex system such as that of plants, higher CO_2 concentrations have a variety of effects which cannot be examined in isolation from one another. In general, monocausal approaches are not very instructive.

Current CO_2 concentrations (355 ppm in 1991) are suboptimal for the photosynthetic rates of C3 plants. Hence, an increase in CO_2 concentrations would increase CO_2 absorption by the plants, and it would increase biomass production by improving photosynthetic rates. In addition, the plants' water utilisation efficiency would also increase since plants close their stomata when exposed to higher CO_2 concentrations. As a result, they would lose less water through transpiration. While different species will vary in their responses, the overwhelming majority of the plants studied showed a CO_2 fertilising effect. Biomass production increases of between 10 and 50 percent were measured when the plants were exposed to a doubling of the CO_2 concentration (13) (25).

C4 plants include maize, millet, sugar cane and other tropical crop plants. For the sake of optimising photosynthesis, these plants have already developed CO_2 accumulation mechanisms. For this reason, they will not benefit at all, or only to a limited extent, from increasing CO_2 concentrations.

In the past, the CO_2 fertilising effect has been regarded as one of the few positive effects of increasing atmospheric CO_2 concentrations. It was suggested that increasing biomass production might help solve global food problems. Furthermore, it was argued that, if more CO_2 was fixed, more carbon would be stored in the form of biomass, which would mitigate the greenhouse effect.

However, numerous effects have been discovered since then which do not lead to an increase in biomass production. Long-term field trials, for instance, have shown that plants will soon get used to higher CO_2 concentrations. However, the plants' ability to transport and process the carbohydrates accumulated is limited. In many cases, a lack of nutrients such as phosphorus has a limiting effect on growth. It has also been demonstrated that the carbon/nitrogen ratio changes if CO_2 concentrations increase. This is likely to reduce the quality of food and animal feed. Another problem may be caused by the preferential treatment of C3 vis-à-vis C4 plants. This might lead to completely different competitive conditions (e.g. more rapid growth of weeds/wild plants). If water supply is limited, it is impossible in many soils to increase photosynthetic rates. There is still a controversial debate about the type and the magnitude of the negative effects to be expected (20). However, it cannot be precluded that the positive effects of CO_2 fertilisation might be offset – or more than offset – by stress factors such as increasing UV-B radiation intensity and air pollution.

Stratospheric ozone depletion will lead to an increase in UV-B radiation intensity and a shift of the absorption edge towards lower wavelenghts. UV-B radiation is mutagenic and compromises the photosynthetic mechanism, the germination rate and general plant growth.

Past studies on the effects of UV-B radiation have been focused on agricultural crop plants. About two-thirds of the roughly 200 species studied proved to be UV-sensitive. These plants showed a decline in biomass production which has not been generally quantified yet. For some plants, the reductions observed were substantial (e.g. 25 percent for soybeans in response to a simulated ozone loss of 25 percent) (26).

In regions affected by the Antarctic ozone hole, biomass production of phytoplankton was found to have decreased by between 6 and 12 percent. Currently, it is suspected that biomass production will decrease by 10 percent in response to increasing UV-B radiation intensity. If this proves to be true, CO_2 emissions can be expected to increase by a few gigatonnes per year. The amount involved would correspond to the annual CO_2 emissions due to the combustion of fossil fuels (27) (28).

Because of the extremely high threat potential, the effects of increasing UV-B radiation will have to be studied in greater detail. Prior to such studies, it is necessary to make exact radiation dose measurements.

The steady increase in concentrations of air pollutants will have severe effects. Because of the predicted increase in global traffic volumes, nitrogen oxide emissions are expected to rise. When combined with simultaneously released hydrocarbons, these nitrogen oxide emissions lead to the formation of tropospheric ozone. In plants, ozone causes damage to the photosynthetic mechanism and to leaves, and it provokes changes in growth rates, yields and quality. Ozone lowers the plants' sensitivity threshold vis-ü-vis other biotic and abiotic stress factors. In the Northern Hemisphere, there are increasingly large areas with high regional ozone concentrations. The duration, intensity and frequency of these "O3 episodes" can vary widely. Because of its phytotoxicity, tropospheric ozone is now regarded as the most important air pollutant, both in the United States and in Europe, although there are once again differences in terms of the sensitivity of specific plant species and varieties (29). Furthermore, ozone is deleterious to human health and to animals.

While the various effects of higher CO_2 concentrations, increasing UV-B radiation intensity and air pollutants are by and large understood, it is very difficult to assess what impact the interaction of these factors will have on plants, animals and soils. Because of our insufficient knowledge in this field, it is currently not possible to make any quantitative statements. There is still a considerable need for reseach in this domain.

3.6.2 Effects of changes in climate parameters (temperatures, precipitation, clouds, etc.)

The following predictions, which have been derived from climate model calculations (see Chapter 3.3), are relevant for agricultural production. Global warming will have the following effects:

– For each degree Celsius of temperature rise, the climatic zones which are suitable for agriculture will move poleward by about 200 to 300 kilometers; and in mountainous regions, they will move higher by 200 meters.
– The frequency and intensity of heavy rainfall will increase at almost all latitudes.
– At mid-latitudes, the number of rainy days will decrease (13).
– At low and mid-latitudes, temperatures will increase more rapidly than at high latitudes.
– Extreme weather events such as droughts, storms and floods will increase in frequency.

Climate change and its effects on agricultural production will vary widely from region to region. There will be a particularly strong impact on semi-arid vegetation zones which respond sensitively to even minor changes in precipitation volumes. These zones will also suffer the most severe climate changes in absolute terms. More specifically, the following regions have been described as particularly sensitive:

In Africa: Maghreb, West Africa, the Horn of Africa, southern Africa.

In Asia: western Arabia, Southeast Asia.

In America: Mexico, Central America, eastern Brazil, Peru.

In addition, these regions will have major adjustment problems because the farmers lack fertile land, irrigation, drought-resistant seeds, technical adaptation potential, and not least, capital and adequate prices for their produce (13).

On the other hand, regions at high latitudes might benefit – in particular in the Northern Hemisphere. Providing that there is safe supply of water and nutrients, rising temperatures would prolong vegetation periods and increase production volumes. Because of the high technological standard in those regions, they will find it easier to adapt to changing economic conditions. In Europe, positive effects might be experienced by the Scandinavian countries, Poland and the northern parts of the former Soviet Union, while the Mediterranean countries may be confronted with major problems in terms of water supply.

In Australia and New Zealand, shifts of vegetation zones will lead to changes in cultivation methods, but not to any major losses.

Changes in the sequence of weather constellations in the course of a day and in the course of a year may lead to changes in the spectrum of noxious animal and plant species and in the incidence of animal and plant diseases. While specific pests may also be diminished due to higher temperatures or prolonged dry periods, living conditions for noxious organisms are, by and large, expected to improve. Higher temperatures, for instance, will shorten the generation times and increase the feeding activities of parasites. Heat-stressed plants will become more susceptible to parasitic attack; milder winters promote the development of frost-sensitive noxious insects. The same applies to animal parasites and diseases.

If farming methods continue to be as intensive as they have been in the past, the consumption of agrochemicals can be expected to increase.

Finally, attention should also be paid to the effects of climate change on symbioses that exist between leguminosae and nodule bacteria, or between trees and mycorrhiza fungi. In these biotic communities, plants supply carbohydrates to soil organisms and receive processable nitrogen and other nutrients in return. It cannot be precluded that higher CO_2 concentrations will promote the activities of symbiotic organisms. This might have a positive effect on biomass production, e. g. in grassland regions (29). However, nitrogen fixation seems to be adversely affected by higher temperatures and increasing concentrations of air pollutants (O_3, NO_x) (13). The opposite trends of these effects illustrate the difficulties involved in making reliable predictions based on our current knowledge, even if only two variables have to be taken into account.

Animal production will be only indirectly affected by climate change. Mammals and birds are generally able to keep their body temperatures constant, independently of atmospheric temperatures. In livestock farming, it may be necessary to keep stables cooler or to heat them less. Changes in the composition of animal feed due to higher temperatures might also have an impact on animal production. Fish production would also be affected (see 3.4.2 Marine ecosystems); at higher latitudes, production volumes might increase (30). However, there will be problems if the oxygen content of the water decreases too much due to increasing temperatures (13) (31).

Positive effects on soil fertility can only be expected from CO_2 fertilisation. A larger plant volume might lead to larger plant residues in the soil, and hence, to an increase in humus production. If humus turnover is accelerated due to global warming, this will temporarily improve the availability of nutrients.

On the other hand, it must be expected that there will be a large number of processes – induced by the greenhouse effect – which might have a highly adverse impact on soils, both quantitatively and qualitatively. Higher temperatures may intensify and accelerate humus turnover due to increasing microbial activity. The organic carbon bound in the soil might be degraded and released on a large scale. This might open up a new source which would release massive amounts of CO_2. However, it is not yet possible to make any quantitative predictions about the magnitude of this effect. A reduction of humus concentrations will adversely affect soil fertility by leading to a deterioration of the physical condition of the soils. Higher temperatures will accelerate soil degradation. The soils will become more susceptible to wind and water erosion. In order to demonstrate the scope of the problem, it should be pointed out that, between 1975 and the year 2000, soil erosion will reduce agricultural production in Africa by one-quarter – irrespective of climate change (32).

In the long term, however, changes in the chemical composition of soils due to increased soil respiration and mineralisation involve the risk that nutrients may be leached out and toxic heavy metals may be mobilised. This, in turn, will lead to groundwater contamination.

If global warming leads to more extensive use of irrigation, this will automatically increase the risk of salinisation. By the mid-Eighties, as much as 24 percent of all irrigated cultivated areas worldwide had been damaged by salinisation; this process will continue because the areas under irrigation will grow and because there is a shortage of high-quality water (32) (33) (34).

The effects which climate change will have on soil fertility and stability should not be underestimated. However, it will be possible to mitigate these effects if sustainable soil cultivation and conservation methods are applied. Considering the importance to be attached to soils – not only because of their high value in agriculture but also because of their role as integral parts of natural ecosystems – there is an urgent need to develop and implement soil preservation concepts.

3.6.3 Socio-economic effects

So far, relatively few studies have dealt with the socio-economic effects of climate change. When assessing these effects, the concept of the "most sensitive regions" can once again be applied. These include large parts of Brazil and Peru, as well as the Sahel zone in Africa, Southeast Asia, and the Asian regions of the former Soviet Union and China.

The economies of these countries are highly dependent on agricultural production, with agriculture accounting for very large proportions of their gross national products. Countries with high population densities are already finding it very difficult to provide sufficient food, water and land. How strong the negative impact of these effects will be in a given country will very much depend on its scope for technological and political adjustment. In the regions most at risk, there is already an imbalance between the local population and the agricultural potential available; and there are no means of adjustment. The farmers lack land, capital, technological know-how and do not earn adequate prices for their produce. Because of low precipitation volumes, the agricultural yields in these regions are already highly dependent on the climate. Any further perturbation will lead to major social problems, food shortages, famines and streams of refugees.

As outlined above, there is no conclusive evidence to the effect that climate change will indeed have a negative impact on global food production. Without any doubt, however, there will be shifts and changes in farming practices. This will, first and foremost, affect the incomes of farmers and the rural employment structure. At a higher level, national food supply and exports may also be jeopardised. The latter may lead to changes in the international food markets' distribution patterns and prices. Changes in regional production costs will also have to be expected. If temperatures rise by 4 °C, for instance, the cost of irrigation in the grain belt of the United States would increase by between 20 and 25 percent. In the central regions of the former Soviet Union, on the other hand, a temperature rise by 1 °C would reduce the production costs of winter wheat by 22 percent (13).

New social structures will have to develop in many countries. For the nomadic tribes in Africa, for instance, a shortage or deterioration of animal feed will lead to greater demand for land (35).

As a final comment, it should be pointed out that the socio-economic effects of climate change will increase the handicap which the developing countries have vis-à-vis the industrialised nations.

References

(1) WMO/UNEP Global Ozone Research and Monitoring Project, no. 25, 1992

(2) Toon, O. B., and Turco, R. P., 1991

(3) Zellner, R., 1992

(4) Wege, K., 1992

(5) Mather, J. H., and Brune, W. H., 1990

(6) Pitari, G., Visconti, G., and Rizi, V., 1991

(7) Enquete Commission on "Preventive Measures to Protect the Earth's Atmosphere", 1990

(8) Liu, S. C., McKeen, S. A., and Madronich, S., 1991; Madronich et al., 1992

(9) Ozon-Symposium, Munich, July 1991

(10) WMO/UNEP (IPCC Working Group I), 1990 and 1992

(11) Statement presented by U. Cubasch at the Enquete Commission's public hearing "Climate I" held on 16-17 January 1992, Commission document no. 12/4-a

(12) Statement presented by H. Flohn at the Enquete Commission's public hearing "Climate I" held on 16–17 January 1992, Commission document no. 12/4-b

(13) WMO/UNEP (IPCC Working Group II), 1990

(14) Statement presented by J. Oerlemans at the Enquete Commission's public hearing "Climate I" held on 16–17 January 1992, Commission document no. 12/4-a

(15) Statement presented by G.P. Hekstra at the Enquete Commission's public hearing "Climate I" held on 16-17 January 1992, Commission document no. 12/4-b

(16) World Wide Fund for Nature – WWF, 1992

(17) Sombroek, 1990

(18) Oral statement presented by G.H. Kohlmaier at the Enquete Commission's public hearing "Climate I" held on 16-17 January 1992

(19) Esser, G., 1989

(20) Bazzaz, F. A., and E.D. Fajer, 1992

(21) Wininger, M., 1992

(22) Statement presented by P. Burschel at the Enquete Commission's public hearing "Climate I" held on 16-17 January 1992, Commission document no. 12/4-i

(23) Statement presented by G.H. Kohlmaier at the Enquete Commission's public hearing "Agriculture II" held on 17-18 February 1992, Commission document no. 12/5

(24) FAO, 1991

(25) Kimball, B. A., 1983

(26) Teramura et al., 1990

(27) Häder, D.P., and R.C. Worrest, 1991

(28) UNEP Report, 1991

(29) Statement presented by H.J. Weigel at the Enquete Commission's public hearing "Agriculture II" held on 17-18 February 1992, Commission document no. 12/5-e

(30) Statement presented by FAO at the Enquete Commission's public hearing "Agriculture II" held on 17-18 February 1992, Commission document no. 12/5-e

(31) Oral statement presented by E. Pfeffer at the Enquete Commission's public hearing "Agriculture II" held on 17-18 February 1992

(32) Brown et al., 1990

(33) Statement presented by D. Sauerbeck at the Enquete Commission's public hearing "Agriculture II" held on 17-18 February 1992, Commission document no. 12/5-a

(34) Statement presented by K. Haider at the Enquete Commission's public hearing "Agriculture II" held on 17-18 February 1992, Commission document no. 12/5-b

(35) Oral statement presented by FAO at the Enquete Commission's public hearing "Agriculture II" held on 17-18 February 1992

4 Current Status of Research

Summary

The increase in the atmospheric concentrations of man-made greenhouse gases will have a greater impact on the climate in the next 100 to 200 years than any other factor such as potential volcanic eruptions or changes in the intensity of solar irradiation. With the exception of a few unanswered questions regarding the role played by clouds, the major internal feedback mechanisms within the climate system are now understood.

It will be necessary to continue research activities in order to improve predictions about changes in regional climate change patterns. Due to the great complexity of the climate system, however, a large degree of uncertainty always remains, since regional and global surprises are practically guaranteed in the case of strictly non-linear couplings. Intensified interdisciplinary research is urgently needed in light of the global nature and the complexity of the issue of climate change and its effects.

There is already a high likelihood today that the equivalent CO_2 concentration will double during the first half of the next century. This will accelerate the rise of mean global temperatures, and it will trigger a redistribution of precipitation. Political decision-makers are urged to initiate countermeasures immediately, since any delay will increase the risk that it will not be possible any more to find a more or less adequate response to control the effects of climate change.

4.1 Facts and Open Questions in the Climate Debate

Predicting climate change involves three main steps:

(a) predicting future emission rates and land use changes,

(b) predicting the amount of trace gases which will remain in the atmosphere,

(c) predicting the climate change based on the inputs from (a) and (b).

The discussion below is limited to steps (b) and (c). Step (a) is controlled by political decision-makers and by general population trends. The uncertainties involved in those two areas, however, have a major impact on the margin of uncertainty associated with climate predictions.

This chapter summarises the most important reliable findings and the major uncertainties in the current debate on global climate change. In addition, the various factors are assessed in terms of their potential impact on the climate, in order to facilitate predictions of future climate trends. The discussion is subdivided into the following topics:

- man-made trace gas emissions,
- internal climate parameters and feedback mechanisms,
- assessment of the sensitivity of various factors affecting the climate system,
- global climate trends,
- regional climate changes and their effects.

4.1.1 Climate potential of man-made trace gas emissions

The man-made increase in the concentrations of long-lived greenhouse gases (CO_2, CH_4, N_2O and CFCs) is still continuing. In the case of methane (CH_4), the rate of increase has slowed in the past few years, for reasons as yet unknown. The atmospheric cycle, particularly the sources and sinks of the various compounds, are not sufficiently understood, so that predictions on the future concentrations of CO_2, CH_4 and N_2O are frought with uncertainty. Methane emissions from rice paddies, N_2O emissions from soils and due to human activities, as well as the global deforestation rates are three cases in point. However, the need to improve our knowledge is particularly pressing with regard to the CO_2 absorption capacity of the oceans and of the terrestrial biosphere. In this context, attention should be paid to feedback mechanisms which may have a major impact on global warming, or on changes in the chemical conditions prevailing in the atmosphere.

The uncertainty involved in our knowledge of the cycles of atmospheric trace gases affects the calculations of direct and indirect global warming potentials (GWPs). The GWP concept can only provide rough estimates of the various gases' relative shares in the man-made greenhouse effect. The difficulties involved are mainly due to the fact that the chemical composition of the atmosphere is constantly changing. This affects both the gases, direct radiative activity, and – via the changes in decomposition rates – the mean atmospheric lifetimes of the various greenhouse gases.

The horizontal and vertical distribution of the gases also plays a major role (e.g. for NO_x, ozone and SO_2) – a point which has not always been taken into consideration in the past.

The relationship between halogenated hydrocarbons (CFCs) and stratospheric ozone depletion, along with its potentially catastrophic effects, is sufficiently understood now. Even though emissions have declined in response to initial measures aimed at reducing the production and consumption of CFCs, an immediate phase-out is urgently needed. In addition, both compounds – ozone and CFCs – also affect the radiation budget of the atmosphere. However, while estimates of the global warming potentials of CFCs are fairly reliable, this applies to a limited extent only to ozone. While ozone is depleted in the stratosphere, it is produced by photochemical reactions in the troposphere – particularly in at northern mid-latitudes. This leads to a major change in vertical ozone distribution. Preliminary estimates of the magnitude of this change suggest a cooling trend for the mid-latitudes of the Northern Hemisphere. This is believed to be partially responsible for the relatively modest warming observed to date. Only a global circulation model involving ozone chemistry could provide a realistic global estimate of this effect, which is at least latitude-dependent. However, such a model is not yet available.

Man-made SO_2 emissions are believed to have a similar effect, i.e. they temporarily compensate for part of the greenhouse effect. The sulphate aerosol particles which form in the atmosphere increase the proportion of scattered radiation in the lowest atmospheric layers, and – when integrated in condensation processes – they also lead to an increase in cloud albedo. However, this is a phenomenon which is at least latitude-dependent, and which is confined to the Northern Hemisphere. There is speculation that this effects also helps to partially compensate for the warming caused by greenhouse gases at northern mid-latitudes.

However, this SO_2 effect fades away very rapidly (i.e. within a few weeks) when emissions are reduced, whereas CO_2 emissions have to be reduced at least by 60 percent in order to freeze atmospheric CO_2 concentrations.

Air traffic plays a significant part in the discussion on man-made sources of radiatively active trace gases. Considerable amounts of radiatively active trace gases such as H_2O, SO_2 and NO_x are released by aircraft in the upper troposphere and lower stratosphere, thus significantly increasing the otherwise low background concentrations of these compounds. The particularities of these gas emissions are that their GWPs are higher in these extremely cold atmospheric layers, that their mean atmospheric lifetimes are generally longer, that they lead to the formation of contrails, and that they may change the ozone profiles in the lower stratosphere and upper troposphere. However, our current knowledge is not yet sufficient to quantify these effects.

4.1.2 Effects of internal climate parameters and possible feedback mechanisms

The term "forcing" describes the adjustment pressure in the climate system which is caused either by changes in internal climate parameters (e.g. ocean circulation patterns) or by changes in external climate parameters (e.g. man-made greenhouse gas emissions). The climate system tries to adjust to this type of "forcing" by changes in internal parameters. These types of partial responses by the system may either enhance the effect of the primary perturbation (positive feedback), or may do the opposite (negative feedback). The most important internal parameters are described below:

– Water vapour

It is a generally accepted fact that water vapour – the most important natural greenhouse gas – tends to enhance the warming induced. A warmer atmosphere will absorb more water vapour, which means that water vapour concentrations will increase even up to the altitude of the upper troposphere (see Chapter 2.2). The positive feedback is particularly pronounced at that altitude. Due to the increasing water vapour concentrations, the proportion of solar radiation absorbed in the atmosphere will also increase, particularly in the lower troposphere.

Along with the radiative effect, it is the release of latent heat (increasing precipitation) – due to increasing water vapour concentrations – in the middle and upper troposphere which is of crucial importance for the intensity of atmospheric circulation.

– Ice/snow albedo

Another mechanism that enhances global warming is the ice/snow albedo feedback. As a planet becomes warmer, its ice and snow sheets will shrink, which means that less solar irradiation will be directly reflected. However, changes in the ice conditions in polar regions are also linked to other meteorological parameters such as the steadiness of the polar vortex, and to changes in cloud cover and precipitation, so that the magnitude of this positive feedback and the rate of the response are still uncertain.

– Clouds

Clouds are currently the greatest factor of uncertainty for climate predictions, although the major components involved in the interactions between radiation and clouds are understood. Table 4.1 provides a summary of the most important changes and of their effects on the climate. However, the cloud formation mechanisms (which are usually small-scale processes) and the complex interactions between radiation and the clouds themselves have not yet been converted with sufficient accuracy to fit large mesh sizes of circulation models. Hence, it is not yet possible to make any reliable predictions on potential cloud feedback effects.

Table 4.1:   Climate Potential of Various Cloud Changes

Cloud change	Effect on climate
Increase in the expanse of low clouds (e.g. stratus clouds)	Cooling
Increase in the expanse of high clouds (e.g. cirrus clouds)	Warming
Increase in cloud altitude	Warming
Increase in the liquid water content in stratus clouds	Cooling
Increase in the liquid water content in cirrus clouds	Warming
Increase in the ratio of cloud droplets to ice particles	— Cooling due to increase in back-scattering — Warming due to increase in drop rate
Increase in the size of cloud droplets or ice particles	Warming

– Changes in ocean circulation

Salinity and temperature are the two factors which control the vertical exchange of ocean water between the ocean surface and the deeper layers of the oceans, particularly at middle and higher latitudes. When changes occur in the hydrological cycle (i.e. evaporation, condensation, precipitation, run-off), the salinity may change so drastically that this may cause

140

changes in the vertical exchange processes and in the geographical regions where these processes occur. In the presence of global warming, a decline in these exchange processes might not only directly affect the oceans' CO_2 absorption capacity, but it might also lead to changes in horizontal ocean circulation patterns. However, it must be kept in mind that the circulation models available today cannot provide reliable predictions of these effects, which could have a major impact on specific regions (e.g. Western Europe). The difficulties involved mainly relate to the description of regional changes in precipitation and run-off fields, and to the fact that the spacial resolution of today's models is still insufficient.

4.1.3 Assessment of the sensitivity of various factors affecting the climate system

An assessment of the sensitivity of the most important parameters which affect the climate can be made by using climate models. Based on the assumption that CO_2 concentrations will double (the assumed initial forcing of the climate system), which would increase by about 4 W/m^2 the heat radiated back from the troposphere to the Earth's surface, the response of the climate system is assessed by means of the increase in global atmospheric surface temperatures. The range of variation between the results of different climate models is a possible yardstick for assessing the uncertainty involved in the predictions.

For this particular computer simulation (i.e. CO_2 doubling), the results vary between 1.5° and 4.5 °C. In the absence of feedbacks in the climate system, all the models predict that the temperature will rise by 1.2 °C if CO_2 concentrations double. The models also show relatively good agreement in the absence of clouds, in which case they predict that the temperature will rise by about 2 °C. The water vapour feedback is a major reason for the increase in sensitivity from 1.2° to 2.0 °C in the absence of clouds.

However, the broad range of variation (between 1.5° and 4.5 °C) is mainly due to differences between the models in the way they deal with clouds. It is generally assumed that the quantitative effect of clouds is probably smaller than suggested by the range of variation mentioned above. Whether the feedback effect of clouds is positive or negative, is still uncertain. Within the range of variation between 1.5° and 4.5 °C, the best estimate given by the IPCC is 2.5 °C.

An evaluation of palaeoclimatic data (temperatures and concentrations of various greenhouse gases over the past 160,000 years) can also be used to estimate the sensitivity of the mean global temperature to a doubling of CO_2 concentrations. Interestingly enough, these estimates range between $2°$ and $4°C$, i.e. they are within the margin of uncertainty estimated on the basis of the models' range of variation. However, what is even more important is that an evaluation of palaeoclimatic data suggests that temperatures will increase by at least $2°C$ in the event of a doubling of CO_2 concentrations, since there is no other explanation for the climate variability observed in the past.

4.1.4 Global climate trends

The most important man-made greenhouse gas is carbon dioxide. It is characterised by a long atmospheric lifetime, by its already very high atmospheric concentration, and by continued rapid growth. Due to human interventions, the climate system is experiencing – for the first time – an increase in atmospheric greenhouse gas concentrations, however, without other climate parameters (e.g. changes in ocean circulation) causing or supporting this development. This means that the "inert" climate system is forced to respond. Climatic history has shown that drastic changes can occur within a matter of 100 years, if the signal triggering the adjustment process is "embedded" in the system. The direction of this man-made change is no longer a subject of scientific controversy: Global surface temperatures will rise with increasing atmospheric concentrations of radiatively active trace gases. The only point which is still subject to debate is the question of when significant climate change will be distinguishable from the natural variability of the current climate, and what the regional distribution will be.

The predominant impact which the man-made greenhouse effect will have on our climate in the next 100 to 200 years is illustrated by the following estimate, which compares the climate impact potentials of the most important external climate parameters (over a period of 100 to 200 years). The yardstick used to estimate the climate potentials is the change caused in the Earth's energy balance – also referred to as "radiative forcing". The following four external factors have been included in this study:

– the forcing of man-made greenhouse gases (i.e. the impact of the man-made greenhouse effect),

– changes in insolation conditions due to periodic changes in solar activity,

– volcanic eruptions (based on the assumption of one major eruption per decade),

– changes in man-made atmospheric sulphate aerosol concentrations.

The forcing caused by man-made greenhouse gases has been calculated for the four IPCC emission scenarios A, B, C and D. These represent the full range of the potential effects of man-made greenhouse gas emissions, depending mainly on the political decisions taken. IPCC scenario A ("business as usual") applies if no action whatsoever is taken to reduce greenhouse gas emissions (except for CFCs, which are assumed to be controlled by the provisions of the Montreal Protocol). Scenarios B, C, and D are based on the assumption that varying measures are adopted to reduce emissions (cf. Chapter 3.2).

Figure 4.1 shows the "radiative forcing" of the four different factors mentioned above for the period from 1990 to the year 2000 (a), and for the period from the year 2000 to the year 2050 (b). The radiative forcing due to man-made greenhouse gas emissions ranges between 0.4 (scenario D) and 0.6 W/m² (scenario A) for the period from 1990 to the year 2000. If a longer time period is examined (in this case, from the year 2000 to the year 2050), the forcing increases to between 1.3 (scenario D) and 3.5 W/m² (scenario A).

In the shorter period of time, the three other external factors are capable of at least partially compensating for the man-made greenhouse effect at regional level. In the longer term, however, the man-made greenhouse effect (which is characterised by constantly increasing atmospheric concentrations, global distribution, and radiative forcing consistently tending in one direction) will outweigh the other factors.

4.1.5   Regional climate change and its effects

Regional climate change can be defined by medium-term trends and/or by changes in statistical data in terms of the frequency and intensity of variations in climate parameters. The effects on the environment and on the living conditions for flora, fauna and human beings can be assessed by means of reliable predictions of regional climate changes. The climate parameters which are most important for predictions (aside from atmospheric surface temperatures) are precipitation, soil moisture, the frequency and intensity of extreme weather events, and, for coastal regions, the rise in sea level. However, it is not yet possible to predict regional climate changes with the required degree of accuracy.

Temperature rise predictions by coupled ocean/atmosphere circulation models – based on the assumption that CO_2 concentrations will increase by 10 percent annually (which includes the effects of the other man-made greenhouse gases) – are in good agreement with one another: they suggest

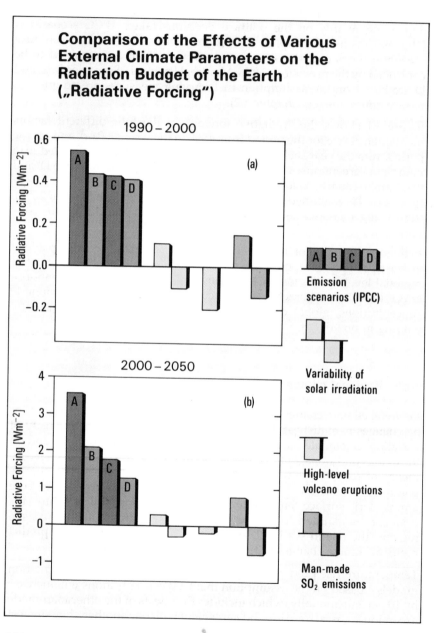

Comparison of the Effects of Various
External Climate Parameters on the
Radiation Budget of the Earth
(„Radiative Forcing")

1990 – 2000

(a)

Radiative Forcing [Wm^{-2}]

A B C D
Emission
scenarios (IPCC)

Variability of
solar irradiation

2000 – 2050

(b)

Radiative Forcing [Wm^{-2}]

High-level
volcano eruptions

Man-made
SO$_2$ emissions

that mean global temperatures will rise by 0.3 °C per decade, with a margin of uncertainty between 0.2° and 0.5 °C. The associated mean sea level rise is estimated at 6 cm per decade (with a margin of uncertainty of between 3 and 10 cm). Generally speaking, the expected warming will be greater above land surfaces than above the oceans. In addition, all models predict that precipitation volumes will increase with increasing temperatures. The increase in precipitation will be most pronounced at higher latitudes, while precipitation will tend to decrease in summer and to increase in winter at mid-latitudes. The predictions with regard to precipitation trends in the tropics are contradictory. It can be expected that there will be substantial regional differences which vary widely in the various models.

Although the quality of predictions on regional climate change is still unsatisfactory, preliminary studies have already been carried out to assess the sensitivity of various environmental systems to potential climate changes (see Chapter 3). These sensitivity analyses help to improve our understanding of the extremely complex interactions between the climate and the environment. The findings of these studies have clearly shown that optimism with regard to the effects of climate change (including the effects on agriculture) does not seem warrented.

4.2 Research Needs

Due to missing fragments in our understanding of the climate, it is not yet possible to make reliable and sufficiently accurate predictions about future development of the climate with all the regional effects involved. These missing fragments are reflected in:

- uncertainties with regard to the natural variability of climate parameters,
- uncertainties involved in the assessment of the sensitivity of internal climate parameters to the external effect – i.e. the forcing – of man-made greenhouse gas emissions (catchword: clouds),

---

◀ *Fig. 4.1: Comparison of the effects of various external climate parameters on the radiation budget of the Earth ("radiative forcing") within a period of (a) 10 years and (b) 50 years.*
The evolution of IPCC emission scenarios A to D (equivalent CO_2 concentrations) over time is shown in Fig. 3.2.
Source: IPCC, WG I, 1990

- uncertainties involved in the assessment of the time-scale of the climate response,
- uncertainties involved in predicting regional climate change, and hence, in assessing potential effects.

The research activities required should concentrate on the following fields which are particularly critical:
- the cycles of radiatively active trace gases,
- the effects of clouds on the radiation budget,
- the hydrological cycle,
- transport processes in the oceans, and the oceans, heat storage capacity,
- ecosystem processes which have an impact on the climate.

In order to improve the current status of our knowledge, it will be necessary to adopt an interdisciplinary research approach which takes into consideration the various relevant physical, chemical and biological processes.

Interdisciplinary research is needed, for example, in the following areas:
- the effects of climate change and of changes in the atmosphere's chemical composition on soils (catchwords: exchange with the atmosphere, soil moisture, soil fertility);
- ecosystem research (catchwords: adjustment problems, rates of adjustment, migration, collapse);
- the adjustment capacity of agriculture (catchwords: cultivation of adapted crops, development of adapted cultivation methods, socioeconomic effects of changes in production, secure food supply, shifts in international markets).

4.2.1 Monitoring and modelling

It is necessary to build up a global network to monitor atmospheric, terrestrial and oceanic data in order to be able to identify the natural variability of climate parameters, as well as their changes and mean trends. The requirements to be met in terms of the quality of the data collected and the equipment of the monitoring stations are high:
- The data collection rate must be sufficiently high, in terms of both space and time, to satisfy the needs of each field of study.

146

- The calibration of the instruments must be reliable.
- The monitoring periods must be sufficiently long.

Examples of important variables are listed below:
- atmospheric chemistry parameters such as the atmospheric mixing ratios of CO_2, OH, CH_4, N_2O, O_3, CFCs and their substitutes, CO, NO_x, VOCs;
- temperature and moisture conditions in the troposphere; wind, precipitation, the radiation budget of the overall system;
- land use, seasonal behaviour of various classes of vegetation, biomass;
- ocean surface temperatures, exchange between ocean surface water and deep-sea water, chlorophyll concentrations;
- ocean ice expanse and thickness, mass budgets of ice sheets in Antarctica and in Greenland.

The prequisite to successfully operating a monitoring network is that the data collected must be immediately subjected to a scientific evaluation – something which has often been neglected in the past. Such evaluation requires not only large computing and memory capacities but also highly skilled personnel.

Climate modelling will have to be improved if the models are to produce reliable predictions. The efficiency of the climate models is still limited by insufficient computing capacity, which in turn limits the spatial resolution, as well as the length of temporal integration steps and the overall integration period. On the other hand, it does not give due consideration to the manifold interactions between the oceans and the atmosphere. In order to be comprehensive, climate simulations must also include the interactions with the biosphere, and the cycles of the most important atmospheric trace gases.

However, the quality of climate predictions depends not only on the capacity of the computers used. The quality of the parametrisation of physical, chemical and biological processes in the models is just as important. For this reason, it is imperative that research activites should be stepped up in this particular area. First of all, however, process studies will have to be carried out in order to improve our understanding of specific physical (chemical or biological) processes by means of monitoring and modelling. On this basis, it will then be possible to include these processes in global circulation models.

All model results require validation. Validation can only be carried out by comparing model predictions with corresponding observations; for this purpose, the quality of the data must be excellent. Good agreement between observations and model predictions does not always guarantee that the physical processes involved were simulated in the model with sufficient accuracy. For this reason, it is necessary to carry out sensitivity comparisons in addition to comparing absolute figures.

4.2.2   Overview of international research activities

We can only hope to master the tasks ahead of us in an international setting. This will require not only substantial financial and human resources, but also a high level of willingness to cooperate and to get involved in an intensive exchange of knowledge and data.

Projects which already exist or which are envisaged for the near future are briefly listed below. The international community of nations is called upon to give their active support to these projects or to facilitate their implementation in the first place, thereby contributing towards considerably reducing the uncertainties which still prevail in the discussion on the climate issue. The success of this international and interdisciplinary research approach will require a high level of coordination. In fact, national research activities should be integrated into this "global change" research.

Table 4.2 provides an overview of the most important international research programmes in the next 10 years.

4.3   Conclusions

Despite the uncertainties – referred to above – with regard to the assessment of climate change and the associated research needs, there is no controversy among scientists about the core findings. In fact, climate parameter trends based on observations are in agreement with climate model predictions.

Atmospheric greenhouse gas concentrations continue to increase, due to a variety of human activities. This will automatically lead to a rapid global warming of the Earth's surface and to a redistribution of precipitation. Today, there is already a high likelihood that the equivalent CO_2 concentration will reach double its pre-industrial level during the first half of the next century. As a result, the rise of mean global temperatures will accelerate. It is still possible, however, to take political decisions in order to prevent equivalent CO_2 concentrations from rising even more rapidly;

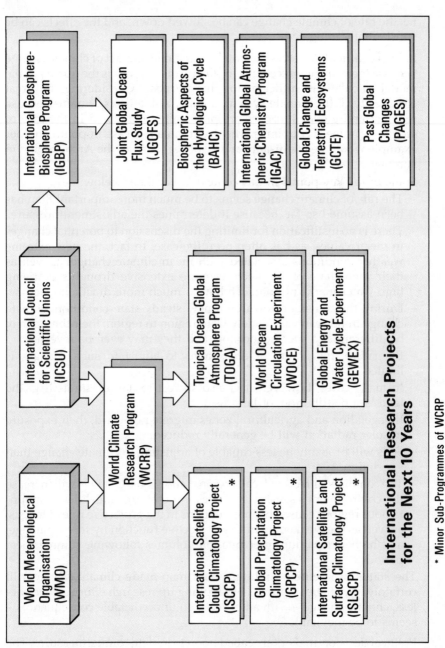

Table 4.2: International research projects for the next 10 years.

i.e. the rate of climate change can be slowed down, and the effects can be substantially mitigated.

It is very difficult to assess the potential regional impact of climate change because there are no precedents in climate history, nor is the quality of the model calculations sufficient for this purpose. Considering the great complexity of the climate system, a major risk always remains because regional and global surprises are practically guaranteed in the case of strictly non-linear couplings. The ozone hole is a case in point; another example would be the disappearance of sea ice from the Arctic region in summer.

Some of the key points in this context are outlined below:

- The rate of climate change seems to be much more important than has been assumed so far, because it determines the adjustment pressure.
- There is no justification for limiting the discussion to potential changes in mean values, as has often been the case. In fact, the new extreme weather conditions associated with mean climate change, as well as their immediate effects such as more extensive droughts or rising high-water marks or both, can have a much more drastic impact.
- During the transition towards a new steady-state condition, climate change trends can vary widely from region to region; their timing may be different at a specific location, and they may even be reversed.
- By nature, the ability of ecosystems to adjust to such changes is limited.
- In many cases, however, it is also subject to natural limits (e.g. the land/sea distribution, or land use).
- If vegetation and agricultural zones migrate poleward, their exposure to solar radiation will be generally reduced.
- Soils will probably be less capable of adjusting to climate change than vegetation.
- The combined effects of local, regional and global changes will increase the environment's sensitivity. Cases in point are landslides in mountainous regions caused by interventions in the protective role of forests, as well as the weakening of this protective function by forest damage, and higher maximum precipitation volumes following summer heat periods.

The status of scientific findings about man-made climate change will certainly have to be improved by stepping up research efforts. Nevertheless, climate change – with all of its often unpredictable consequences – seems to be inevitable.

Political decision-makers are called upon to initiate countermeasures. The urgency of such actions is underlined by the accompanying socio-economic conditions which are already very difficult now and which are bound to deteriorate further in the future. The call for immediate action is motivated by the concern that any delay will increase the risk that it will no longer be possible to find a more or less adequate response to control the effects of climate change.

4.4 Interdisciplinary Research

In view of the imminent climate catastrophe, there have been regular calls – not only from natural scientists but also from humanities scholars and social scientists – for an intensification of interdisciplinary research, since findings from specific disciplines have to be put in perspective because of the global nature and the complexity of the climate issue. While a very intensive, fruitful discourse has already been initiated among natural scientists from various specialised fields, and among humanities scholars and social scientists, there has been very little contact between these two fields of research. However, it is this type of interdisciplinary research which would make it easier for scientists to present integrated climate protection concepts to politicians, because knowledge of the interdependencies between the scientifically studied climate processes and the socio-economically analysed effects of climate change would also make it easier to understand the effects of political actions.

With regard to the analysis of the imminent climate change, natural scientists are further advanced in their findings than social scientists because it has only been in the past few years that the available socio-economic models – which had been designed for other applications – have been modified to meet the requirements involved in analysing climate change. However, more studies will have to be conducted, and new approaches will have to be developed, not only in order to improve our understanding of the socio-economic effects of climate change, but also in order to improve our assessment of the impact of the countermeasures adopted. From the outset, the new socio-economic approaches should have an interdisciplinary design. This should help to obtain findings, as soon as possible, which do justice to the global and complex interdependencies involved; and it should help to satisfy the increasingly urgent demands – being made by scientists and politicians – for expeditious and efficient action (1) (2).

References

(1) IEA, hearing held on 28–29 January 1992; written statements I, p. 24 et seq.
(2) OECD, hearing held on 28–29 January 1992; written statements II, pp. 7, 18 and 20–22

5 Climate Policy

5.1 International Agreements and Implementation Strategies

A number of international agreements are aimed at controlling the greenhouse effect and putting an end to stratospheric ozone depletion.

5.1.1 Vienna Convention for the Protection of the Ozone Layer

On 22 March 1985, following an extended period of negotiations, twenty-one countries – including the Federal Republic of Germany and six other Members States of the European Community – signed the "Vienna Convention for the Protection of the Ozone Layer". The draft of the Convention had been drawn up by a group of experts from the United Nations Environment Programme.

By August 1988, the required number of states (twenty) had also ratified the Convention, so that it entered into force for the parties to the agreement. The Convention became effective for the Federal Republic of Germany on 1 January 1989.

The signatory states have committed themselves to take all appropriate action needed to protect human health and the environment from adverse effects of man-made changes in the ozone layer, and to prevent repercussions on the climate.

The Vienna Convention is a framework agreement which does not specify concrete protective measures. These are to be supplemented in subsequent protocols.

5.1.2 The Montreal Protocol on Substances that Deplete the Ozone Layer

On 22 September 1987, the representatives of 24 countries and of the European Community signed the Montreal Protocol as the first follow-up agreement to the Vienna Convention.

The Montreal Protocol entered into force on 1 January 1989 following ratification by the required eleven countries – which accounted for two-thirds of the global consumption of substances controlled under the Protocol. The Montreal Protocol specifies reduction timetables for eight ozone depleting substances which are subdivided into two groups in the Protocol's annexes. Group I includes the fully halogenated CFCs 11, 12, 113, 114 and 115, while group II consists of the halons 1211, 1301 and 2402.

The provisions of the Protocol refer to the production and the domestic consumption of controlled substances, including imports and exports. According to the reduction timetable which applies to group I, CFC production and consumption will have to be frozen at 1986 levels between July 1989 and June 1993.

In the ensuing period from mid-1993 to 1999, production and consumption will have to be gradually reduced, ultimately reaching 50 percent of 1986 levels.

The provisions applying to halons (group II) merely stipulate that production and consumption of these substances must be reduced to 1986 levels by 1992, and that these levels must be maintained in subsequent years. In addition, the parties to the Protocol have undertaken to facilitate access for developing countries to environmentally safe alternative substances and to the technologies required. Furthermore, they have undertaken to assist the developing countries in making expeditious use of such alternative substances.

Many aspects of the Montreal Protocol have been the subject of criticism. A number of ozone depleting substances were not included in the Protocol; exports of such substances were explicitly excluded from its provisions; and extensive exemptions were allowed for developing countries.

However, the Montreal Protocol is not the closing chapter on the subject. In fact, it was intended to be open-ended so that, later, new findings on the level of ozone depletion could be taken into account. It also provides for amendments to allow for the future development of substitute products, as well as alternative technologies required to manufacture such new substances.

The annual meetings of the parties to the Protocol provided for in the agreement serve as a framework for review, so that the Convention can be adapted to the latest developments.

5.1.3 Strengthening the Montreal Protocol

At the second meeting of the parties to the Protocol, which was held in London in June 1990, the provisions of the Montreal Protocol were considerably tightened.

The conference decided that the production and consumption of certain ozone-depleting substances should be reduced in accordance with the timetable shown in Figure 5.1.

Developing countries are entitled to delay their compliance with the respective reduction stages by 10 years.

Furthermore, the strengthened provisions prohibit imports of controlled substances to, and exports of these substances from, countries which are not parties to the Protocol. The agreement reached in London for the first time lays down the developing countries' right to obtain a speedy transfer of environmentally sound alternative substances and technologies from the industrialised nations.

This is linked to the developing countries' right to obtain financial assistance from a new fund, known as the "Multilateral Fund", which will be financed by the industrialised nations. The financial volume of the fund will amount to US$ 160 million when completed in 3 years' time.

When India and China become parties to the Montreal Protocol, special provisions will go into effect. At that juncture, the financing of the Multilateral Fund will be increased by US$ 40 million in each case to a total of US$ 240 million. China declared its accession to the Protocol in 1991.

The fund is governed by the parties to the Protocol. An Executive Committee, which has been established to implement the decisions taken, has been given the following tasks:

– to draw up financial regulations and a statute,
– to monitor and supervise the administration of the fund,
– to monitor expenditure,
– to grant approval in the case of projects exceeding a total of volume of US$ 250,000.

The composition of the Executive Committee is based on full parity, with 7 members from developing countries and the same number representing industrialised nations. The fund is financed according to the UN scale of assessment, which means that the share to be contributed by the Federal Republic of Germany amounts to 9.2 percent.

The amendments adopted at the London meeting of the parties to the Montreal Protocol represent the first global agreement which specifies

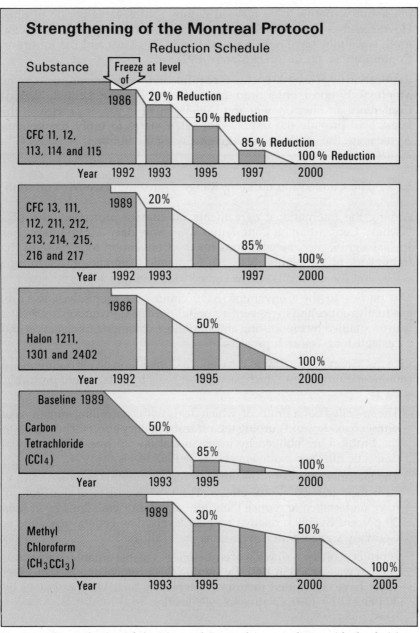

Fig. 5.1: Strengthening of the Montreal Protocol in accordance with the decision taken by the parties to the Protocol at their second meeting held from 27 to 29 June 1990 in London

phase-out scenarios to be realised within a foreseeable period of time. However, these provisions are not yet legally binding at international level, since they have only been ratified by 17 states and the European Community so far (as of 25 March 1992).

Ratification by at least 20 parties is required before the amendments to the Montreal Protocol enter into force. Hopefully, the United Nations Conference on Environment and Development in Rio de Janeiro, at the latest, will provide the impetus for other states to ratify the London Agreement, thus making the Agreement legally binding.

5.1.4 The Convention on Long-Range Transboundary Air Pollution

Among the international agreements on climate protection, the 1979 "Geneva Convention on Long-Range Transboundary Air Pollution" has special significance. Negotiations for the Convention took place in the framework of the United Nation's Economic Commission for Europe (ECE) and the Convention was signed in November 1979.

The parties to the Convention have committed themselves to curb, gradually reduce and to prevent air pollution. The Convention's objective is to be attained by monitoring air pollution, exchanging information and by establishing research projects.

Like the Vienna Convention, the Geneva Convention on air pollution is a framework agreement which serves as a basis for subsequent protocols, such as:

- The so-called Sofia Protocol, which deals with controlling emissions of nitrogen oxides, and curbing their transboundary effects. The parties to the Protocol are obliged by international law to freeze their annual domestic nitrogen oxide emissions at 1987 levels by 1994.
- The Helsinki Protocol is designed to reduce sulphur emissions and to curb their transboundary effects. The twelve parties to the Protocol have undertaken to reduce their annual sulphur emissions by at least 30 percent by 1993, relative to 1980 levels. The Federal Republic of Germany signed both conventions on 9 July 1985.
- A protocol on the reduction of emissions of volatile organic compounds (VOCs) was signed in 1991. By signing this protocol, the ECE member states have committed themselves to reduce their VOC emissions by 30 percent by 1999, relative to 1988 levels.

5.1.5 The European Energy Charter

On 16-17 December 1991, the commonly agreed upon text of a European Energy Charter was signed in The Hague by 46 countries including the Western European countries, the United States, Canada, Japan, Australia, as well as Central and Eastern European countries and the CIS.

The Charter is intended to provide a solid foundation for closer cooperation between the countries concerned in the energy industry, as well as in the production, distribution and use of energy, in order to promote information and technology transfer, as well as energy efficiency, energy conservation and sustainable use of energy. While the Charter is not legally binding, its political declarations of intent are to be substantiated by legally binding agreements to be negotiated in future.

In these subsequent agreements, particular attention will have to be paid to the climate protection issue.

5.1.6 Future agreements

The agreements mentioned above represent the current status of international codification in the field of climate protection.

In addition, various international bodies are currently discussing more stringent agreements. The following overview is intended to highlight the most important activities in this field without claiming to be exhaustive.

5.1.6.1 Climate Convention

The results of the Second World Climate Conference held in Geneva from 29 October to 7 November 1990 have had a major impact on the development of an international climate convention. Scientists and politicians from over 130 countries participated in the conference, discussing priorities and the development of a future world climate programme.

The conference participants emphasised that there had to be an immediate global response to the climate threat, however, without jeopardising the opportunities for all countries to achieve sustainable development, and that preventive action should be taken on the basis of current knowledge. It was also acknowledged that the international community of nations shared common, albeit differentiated responsibility for the protection of the climate.

However, the conference issued no explicit statements on reduction targets and how binding they should be, or on instruments of climate policy.

Negotiations on a convention designed to provide comphrehensive climate protection are now taking place in the framework of the Intergovernmental Negotiating Committee (INC). Participants in the INC negotiations are UN member states and a number of international organisations and non-governmental organisations (NGOs).

The countries trying to reach a legally binding agreement follow two different schools of thought concerning the formulation of a convention:

According to the European Community and its Member States, as well as the EFTA countries, legally binding responsibilities should be laid down concerning the containment and reduction of greenhouse gas emissions, and regarding the preservation and improvement of carbon dioxide (CO_2) resevoirs and sinks.

Other countries feel that the Climate Convention – like the Vienna Convention – should represent a framework agreement which should provide a basis for subsequent specialised protocols which should define legally binding provisions designed to contain CO_2 emissions.

5.1.6.2 Forestry Convention

At the second and third preparatory conferences (March/April, August/ September 1991) for the United Nations Conference on Environment and Development in Brazil, it was agreed that a statement should be adopted at the Brazil conference, which would include a comprehensive declaration of principles, strategies and proposed measures on the management, protection and maintenance of forests worldwide.

In view of the threat to the forest stand observed in all climate zones, a convention limited to the protection of tropical forests would make no sense from a global perspective.

Furthermore, tropical countries would view a regionally limited convention as being discriminatory.

Negotiations on a Forestry Convention can begin in late autumn 1992, after the 47th General Assembly of the United Nations has issued a mandate for this purpose.

The envisaged Convention's success in providing effective climate protection hinges, to a large extent, on the industrialised nations' willingness and ability to equip the developing countries with the financial means required to stop – or even reverse – the process of destruction of the Earth's forests.

5.2   European Community

5.2.1   The evolution of EC environmental policy

The cornerstone of EC environmental policy, which was initially geared towards solving local environmental problems, was laid in the early Seventies. However, this initial concept was extended fairly soon, when it became apparent that environmental pollution does not halt at national boundaries. Due to the greenhouse effect, the ozone hole and the international erosion of the gene pool, environmental policy has shifted its focus toward the global dimension of environmental issues.

The EC feels that it has a special responsibilty to solve these problems. This responsibilty must be seen against the background that the industrialised nations have often been the main perpetrators of what are now pressing problems. The responsibility of the European Community is interpreted so broadly that assistance given to developing countries in order to improve their environmental conditions, for instance, is considered to be within the scope of possible EC actions.

In addition, the European Community views itself as a catalyst for important environmental developments (1).

5.2.2   EC actions for climate protection – recent developments

5.2.2.1 CO_2 and other greenhouse gases

At a meeting held on 29 October 1990, the energy and environmental ministers of the EC adopted a concrete quantitative target, according to which CO_2 emissions were to be stabilised at 1990 levels by the year 2000.

The ministers called upon the EC Commission to submit to the Council proposals for concrete action. The strategy paper of the EC Commission was adopted on 25 September 1991.

The EC Council debated the proposal submitted by the Commission at a Council meeting held in mid-December 1991. The basic concept developed by the Commission – including, for the first time, a proposal for an energy/CO_2 tax – met with the Council's approval. However, the Council returned the proposal to the Commission, requesting formal proposals for more concrete, detailed measures. Furthermore, the Council pointed out that the results of the meeting of the Council of Economics and Finance Ministers should also be taken into consideration.

At its meeting a few days later, the Council of Economics and Finance Ministers did not comment on the content of the Commission's proposal; it merely instructed the working group on tax issues to resume deliberations and to take into consideration the decision adopted by the energy and environmental ministers at their meeting. The results were to be submitted to the Council for deliberation before the UN Conference on Environment and Development (2) (3) (4).

In addition to the EC's policy of explicitly limiting CO_2 emissions – which is just in the process of being developed – a number of other measures have been adopted, for example, in the fields of energy efficiency and energy conservation, which also have an impact on emissions of CO_2 and other greenhouse gases:

– One focal point of EC environmental and climate policy is the energy sector; the objective pursued here is to increase energy efficiency and energy conservation. R&D and demonstration programmes (such as JOULE and THERMIE) represent the cornerstones of this policy. Along with promoting energy conservation and increasing the efficiency of the energy sources mainly being used today, EC energy policy also promotes innovative and renewable energy sources. Recently the EC has expanded its support beyond basic research to include assistance for launching products on the market (the ALTENER programme). Furthermore, the EC established the SAVE programme to promote energy efficiency and to test innovative planning techniques (least-cost planning). In order to maximise the impact of EC actions in the energy sector, the Community cooperates with partners worldwide. The most intensive contacts are those with countries in the Second and Third World.

– The reduction of emissions (not only of CO_2 emissions) in the transport sector through energy conservation and energy efficiency represents another major priority of EC climate policy. Several Member States have already submitted national proposals for an EC directive on limiting CO_2 emissions from motor vehicles.

– Two of the EC's research programmes, EPOCH and STEP, are designed to study climate and atmospheric processes. They also deal with the impact of climate change on ecosystems. Another objective of these programmes is to facilitate a more systematic climate policy by improving scientific knowledge (5) (6).

The concrete implementation of the CO_2 reduction strategy envisaged by the EC is based not least on stepping up activities in the areas mentioned above.

Both in terms of its objectives and in terms of its approaches to solutions, the basic EC concept resembles the Climate Protection Programme of the Federal Republic of Germany.

- The measures cover all the sectors which affect the climate: households and small-scale users, industry, the energy sector, transport, as well as forestry and agriculture.
- The strategy is subdivided into three fields of action:
  - non-fiscal measures
  - fiscal measures
  - supplementary programmes in the EC Member States carried out according to the principle of subsidiarity.

The category entitled "non-fiscal measures" covers a number of different approaches, including R&D programmes and regulatory interventions, as well as voluntary measures and specific regulations applying to individual sectors.

In the field of research and development, there are plans to step up projects such as THERMIE and JOULE in future.

The measures envisaged for the energy sector will continue to follow the lines of the energy policy which is already being pursued. Energy conservation is to be facilitated, in particular, for private households and industry.

The need for action in the transport sector has been recognised, particularly in view of this sector's dynamic growth and massive, negative external effects. What is needed, along with the use of the most efficient technologies available, are efforts in the field of structural policy. The modal split should be modified (getting away from automobiles and turning more towards rail and waterway transport), in conjunction with the promotion of intermodal transport. A network of high-speed railways across Europe (lines are to be newly constructed or extended along key routes) can make a contribution in this context.

In addition, a change in attitude should be promoted on the part of citizens, in order to reduce private transport, so that the proportion of remaining non-public transport is less harmful to the climate. This can be done, for example, through consistent enforcement of speed limits.

While acknowledging the importance of the proposed non-fiscal measures, the Commission has come to the conclusion that this set of measures is not sufficient for attaining the defined objective of stabilising CO_2 emissions. Fiscal measures will have to be applied in addition. The objective is to increase the price of energy so that the external costs are internalised, i.e., the polluter will be held accountable for the costs of the damage caused.

In addition to a combined energy/CO_2 tax – one component of the tax is linked to energy consumption, the other is a tax levied on CO_2 emissions, where the energy component should not account for more than 50 percent of the overall tax – a scheme for taxing motor vehicles according to their emissions has also been discussed. Consumption of fossil fuels for non-energy purposes and renewable energy sources (except for large-scale hydropower stations) would be exempt from the energy/CO_2 tax.

Certain measures may be taken to ensure that the competitive position of companies within the EC countries is not endangered; the "climate tax" will be based on the principle of "neutrality of revenue" (cf. Annex, List of Terms), and exemptions will possibly be granted to some energy-intensive and export-oriented sectors, as long as major trade partners such as Japan and the USA have not adopted similar regulations.

In order to minimise the problems involved in adapting to the new situation, the tax rate will be increased progressively. The tax will be levied for the first time on 1 January 1993 at US\$ 3 per barrel oil. It will then be increased by one dollar annually until the year 2000. Collecting the tax will be within the responsibility of each EC Member States, which means that the mode of determining the neutrality of the tax revenue will also be decided at national level.

The likelihood that Member States would accept the "climate tax" was increased by including provisions allowing for a flexible adaptation of the tax to uncertain future global developments, such as economic upswings and downswings or changes in energy prices. It will be possible to lower the tax if required by future economic developments, or if the trend in CO_2 emissions improves sufficiently.

No formal decision has been taken so far on the energy/CO_2 tax proposed by the EC Commission as an instrument of European climate policy.

Efforts are being made to complement the EC measures by means of national programmes which will have to be adapted to the specific prevailing in each Member State. The general scope of these measures is identical to that of the instruments used at Community level, and it is also aimed at reducing emissions of CO_2 and of other greenhouse gases.

The envisaged national actions, timetables and possible transfers among the Member States should be consistent with each other and compatible with the measures planned at EC level (7).

5.2.2.2   Ozone-depleting gases

– The European Community began to deal with the issue of ozone depleting substances in the early Eighties when it introduced controls on the CFCs 11 and 12.

  The ratification process of the Vienna Convention (1985) by the European Community lasted until 1988; the provisions laid down in the Montreal Protocol were ratified at the same time, thereby imposing controls on the production and consumption of five CFCs and three halons. However, these provisions fell short of the recommendations made at the Climate Conference (World Conference on Atmospheric Change) held in Toronto in 1988.

  When the European Community incorporated the revised version of the Montreal Protocol (which had been adopted in June 1990 at the Second Meeting of the Parties to the Montreal Protocol) in the corresponding EC Regulation, it also took the opportunity to tighten the timetable with regard to the ban of CFCs and of carbon tetrachloride by several years, in fact accelerating it to mid-1997 and to the end of 1997, respectively. The use of H-CFCs was limited to a maximum of 5 percent of 1989 consumption levels of CFCs. The EC phase-out requirements for halons and methyl chloroform are analogous to the revised version of the Montreal Protocol.

  The EC called for further revisions of the Montreal Protocol, in keeping with stricter Community regulations. The European Community has also expressed its willingness to grant assistance and to help developing countries in phasing out controlled substances.

  Emission reduction targets for the ozone depleting substances nitrous oxide and methane, which are caused by activities in the energy, waste disposal and agricultural sectors, are to be specified by 1994 at the latest.

– Three voluntary agreements concluded with industries which are major CFC consumers complement the precisely defined phase-out time-tables that have already been adopted. The sectors involved are: the refrigeration industry, the foamed plastics industry, and the aerosol industry.

163

– Scientific knowledge of the ozone depletion process is to be deepened by research programmes in the fields of climatology and stratospheric chemistry. Two examples of such programmes are the EPOCH and STEP projects mentioned above (8) (9).

The EC negotiating position for the fourth meeting of the Parties to the Montreal Protocol, which will be held in Copenhagen, has become more stringent in the light of the latest findings – i.e. the danger of an ozone hole developing in the Northern Hemisphere. The EC therefore suggests that the production and consumption of CFCs, halons, carbon tetrachloride and methyl chloroform should be prohibited as early as by 1995.

5.2.3 EC position on the United Nations Conference on Environment and Development

The EC wants to see to it that, along with a strong climate framework convention, two protocols will be adopted at the conference: one designed to limit CO_2 emissions, and another one designed to preserve the tropical forests. Assistance for the developing countries is envisaged to enable them to comply with their contractual obligations (10).

5.3 Federal Republic of Germany

5.3.1 Energy

On 13 June 1990, the German Federal Government decided to impose a substantial reduction of energy-related CO_2 emissions. The envisaged reduction target of 25 percent was orientated towards the 1987 emission levels. On 7 November 1990, following German unification and the accession of five new federal states, the German Government confirmed the 25-percent reduction target for the old federal states, and envisaged a much higher reduction target for the new federal states. In doing so, the German Federal Government followed the recommendations which had been made by the preceding Enquete Commission on "Preventive Measures to Protect the Earth's Atmosphere".

In order to implement the Cabinet decision adopted on 13 June 1990, the German Federal Government established an Interministerial Task Force on CO_2 Reductions, composed of representatives from 10 ministries under the chairmanship of the Federal Ministry of the Environment, Nature Conservation and Nuclear Safety. In December 1991, the Interministerial Task Force on CO_2 Reductions submitted a status report with proposals for decisions, and expressed its support for the decision to reduce CO_2 emissions by between 25 and 30 percent. One of the purposes of this task force is to ensure the active support of the various federal states for the prevention of CO_2 emissions. If the decision on reducing CO_2 emissions is to be implemented, it is indispensable for federal, state and local authorities to participate actively.

The following measures are being prepared, or have already been adopted, at federal level (11):

– In the current legislative period, the *Energiewirtschaftsgesetz* (Energy Management Act) will be amended to include sustainable management of resources and environmental protection in the act's catalogue of objectives.

– The new *Bundestarifordnung Elektrizität* (Federal Survey of Electricity Charges), which entered into force in early 1990, offers equitable incentives for efficient electricity use by introducing more linearised electricity rates.

– The *Stromeinspeisungsgesetz (Gesetz über die Einspeisung von Strom aus erneuerbaren Energien in das öffentliche Netz)* (Electricity Sales Act – Act on the Sale of Electricity Generated from Renewable Energy Sources to the Public Grid) provides for an obligation to purchase electricity generated from renewable energy sources, and it lays down the minimum compensation to be paid for such electricity. In fact, the minimum to be paid for plants with power outputs of up to 500 kilowatts shall be at least 75 percent of the average proceeds per kilowatt-hour of electricity sold by power supply companies to all final consumers. A higher compensation shall be due for electricity generated from wind or solar energy; the minimum compensation for electricity from plants with outputs of more than 500 kilowatts shall be only 65 percent of this amount. The purpose of this provision is to improve the competitive situation for renewable energy sources. External effects caused by the generation of electricity from fossil fuels are not allocated to the latter. Consequently, the renewable energy sources, which are environmentally more sound, are at a disadvantage in competition. This disadvantage can be offset by internalising the external effects – i.e. allocating the full costs – or it can be neutralised by financial promotion.

– In the buildings sector, an amendment to the *Wärmeschutzverordnung* (Ordinance on Heat Conservation) is being prepared with the objective of achieving low-energy house standards for all new buildings. In addition, stricter provisions are being drawn up for the Heizungsanlagenverordnung (Ordinance on Heating Installations) and the Kleinfeuerungsanlagenverordnung (Ordinance on Small Furnaces). The purpose of these measures is to reduce the consumption of energy used for space heating, which is the largest homogenous final energy consumption sector.

- An ordinance on the use of waste heat in trade and industry is currently being drawn up. Under this ordinance, heating plant operators will be obliged to develop concepts for a more efficient use of the (waste) heat generated.

- The envisaged amendment to the *Honorarordnung für Architekten und Ingenieure* (Schedule of Fees for Architects and Engineers) is designed to enable architects and engineers to charge for planning services which help to reduce the energy consumption – and hence, the emissions – caused by the use of buildings.

- There are plans to put more emphasis on energy efficiency issues and the use of renewable energy sources in the vocational training and continuing education of certain occupational groups. For this purpose, the respective curricula will be modified, and these modifications will be translated into educational practice.

- The district heating networks in the new federal states will be modernised in such a way that it will be possible to preserve and obtain long-term viable structures. A multiannual investment promotion programme sponsored by the federal government and by state-level authorities is intended to spur investments of DM 1 billion.

- In addition, there are programmes designed to promote the construction of wind-driven power stations (with funds that are sufficient to finance 250 megawatts of electricity generation capacity) and of photovoltaic systems ("1,000 roofs programme" with sufficient funds to sponsor a maximum of 2,250 installations).

The implementation of this set of measures will help to achieve only a small proportion (slightly more than 10 percent) of the CO_2 emission reductions envisaged by the German Federal Government and by the predecessor of the current Enquete Commission (12). The reduction target will only be attained if current measures are intensified, if more measures are added, and if the pace at which existing obstacles are eliminated is accelerated.

The main focus of actions initiated at the level of the federal states is on the promotion of low-energy-consumption buildings.

In addition, almost all federal states grant investment subsidies designed to promote the use of renewable energy sources.

Since vocational training and continuing education is traditionally the prerogative of the federal states, there are activities in nine federal states in the field of continuing education for architects and craftsmen.

166

Energy agencies have been established in several federal states (e.g. North-Rhine Westphalia, Saarland, Lower Saxony, Hesse). It is the task of these agencies to facilitate energy efficiency, in particular in the sector of small-scale users (mainly small and medium-size enterprises, as well as public buildings), by offering advice and third-party funds, and by practising energy conservation. Because of the separation between investment and operating cost budgets, and because of lack of information or insufficient awareness of energy matters, many energy consumers do not even carry out energy conservation measures that make economic sense.

Moreover, energy management concepts have also been developed by many regional and local authorities. In ten federal states, funds have been earmarked specifically for the promotion of co-generation. In their energy management concepts, the regional and local authorities involved have outlined energy conservation possibilities for their areas of supply, and they have specified measures designed to make use of the energy conservation potentials identified. These management concepts can be used as a basis for a future integrated energy planning approach.

Some local authorities have defined emission reduction targets for greenhouse gases in the area for which they are responsible. The city of Schwerte, for instance, has decided to reduce CO_2 emissions by 30 percent by the year 2000 (relative to 1989). The steps required to attain this target have already been defined. Progress will be assessed on an annual basis, and the results of these reviews will be presented in interim reports.

5.3.2 Transport

Because of increasing mobility needs, enormous efforts will have to be made in the required short and medium-term perspective in order to reduce CO_2 emissions by 25 percent, as envisaged by the German Federal Government.

Transport is a sector which is not only particularly problematic but also highly sensitive, because the fact that transport has acquired such eminent importance in terms of energy consumption and emissions is due, not least, to its broad range of functions in industry and society.

The transport sector needs fundamental re-orientation – with the objective in mind to develop a regional planning and transport system which should be as environmentally and climatically sound as possible. For this purpose, the key principle of transport policy – which is to create the preconditions for the most cost-effective transport operations possible –

167

will have to include environmental costs. Transport services will have to be geared towards the objective of "environmental soundness".

More specifically, the objectives to be pursued are:

- to avoid, re-route, guide and reduce traffic, and
- to develop better technology.

It will be necessary to make further environmentally sound improvements in vehicle technology. A decrease of fuel consumption – e.g. down to 5 liters per 100 kilometers (or about 47 miles per gallon) in everyday traffic – would considerably help to reduce emissions from the transport sector.

In order to support efforts aimed at reducing exhaust gas emissions, in particular NO_x emissions, the *Deutsche Versuchsanstalt für Luft- und Raumfahrt (DLR)* (German Aerospace Research Establishment) was asked to conduct a research programme on "Atmospheric Pollutants" consisting of the two sub-programmes "Atmospheric Research" and "Engine Technology". The main focus of the "Engine Technology" sub-programme, which is aimed at finding ways to reduce engine emissions of pollutants, is on combustion chamber processes. New concepts such as lean combustion and adjustable rich/lean mix engines are promising developments which offer both useful and technically feasible solutions for future air transport.

However, it is already foreseeable from today's perspective that strategies which are limited to introducing technological or operational changes in specific modes of transport will not be sufficient in order to master the task at hand, and to cope with the tremendous challenges of the climate issue.

For this reason, the national implementation strategy will have to include the question of mobility, which is a highly sensitive political, economic and social issue.

Transport policy will therefore also have to incorporate non-technical measures to guide, re-route and avoid traffic, i.e. increasing the attractiveness of rail transport, improving the service quality and the attractiveness of public metropolitan passenger transport systems, especially in and between conurbations. The need for such measures is all the more urgent since traffic volumes will be increasing, not only because of German unification and the opening of Central and Eastern Europe but also because of the imminent completion of the internal market of the EC.

The national implementation strategy will also have to include the field of local traffic prevention by means of regional planning. At European level, current goods transport concepts will have to be subjected to a critical review, and major efforts will have to be made in order to develop an efficient all-European rail transport policy. In fact, rail transport could help to compensate for regional disparities.

Transport perspectives will be particularly important with a view to the integration of the Eastern European countries in a larger Europe. Either it will be possible to transfer production sites and industrial operations into these countries – with all the implications in terms of cross-border traffic flows – or the traditional, densely populated conurbations will have to face increasing traffic and agglomeration problems because of continuing immigration.

Since the transport sector is closely intertwined with the other sectors of society and of industry, the conclusion for the implementation strategies is that it will be easier to argue effectively in favour of the "global climate objective" and to attain this objective, if other related sectors are also taken into consideration.

All the national strategic approaches mentioned above will have to be supported by corresponding international actions. It should not be possible to evade more stringent requirements imposed at national level by transferring operations to neighbouring or more remote foreign countries.

Global coordination, or supplementing national implementation strategies at global level, is of top priority – not only because of the global character of the climate issue, which can only be mastered by supranational action, but also because of the undesirable evasive actions mentioned (e.g. environmental dumping).

5.3.3 Agriculture and forestry

The mean global contribution of modern, industrialised agriculture to the man-made greenhouse effect amounts to about 15 percent. Hence, there is an urgent need for action in this sector, as well. This is also underlined by the fact that there is a global trend towards increasingly energy-intensive farming methods. This means that energy consumption is increasing more rapidly than agricultural yields.

One of the fundamental objectives of an EC-wide agricultural reform is to promote ecologically sustainable farming practices. An accelerated transition towards organic farming methods could help prevent further environmental damage, avoid emissions of radiatively active gases from agriculture, and improve the ability of agricultural ecosystems to adjust to the effects of climate change. This is to be achieved by directly sponsoring incomes instead of indirectly promoting products, while at the same time reducing production volumes.

In 1992, the land set-aside programme is to be extended in the framework of the EC's agricultural reform. Programmes for the cultivation of reproductive raw materials have also been developed for the areas concerned. Such raw materials could be used to replace industrial feedstocks and fossil fuels. However, the production of renewable raw materials only makes sense if the energy balance can be proven to be positive. The purpose of programmes designed to promote extensive farming practices is to help preserve species, promote permanent storage of carbon in biomass, and protect water resources. The negotiations on the EC agricultural reform have not yet produced any concrete results.

The introduction or continuing promotion of ecologically sustainable soil cultivation methods and of set-aside programmes can help to reduce carbon losses. Because of the substantial threat that soils are exposed to if the climate changes, there is an urgent need to develop viable soil preservation concepts.

Wherever possible, re-afforestation can help to increase the amount of carbon stored in biomass and to augment humus concentrations in soils.

In the Federal Republic of Germany, the forestry sector supports the function of forests as a CO_2 sink by preserving and increasing forest areas, and more importantly, by increasingly introducing natural forest management systems.

In the field of livestock farming, there is a considerable potential for reducing methane and ammonia emissions, in particular from large-scale livestock farms.

Current promotional programmes are aimed at tying animal density rates to area requirements, thereby reducing the number of animals. Environmentally sound farming must include the use of domestic animal feed; ecologically harmful imports of animal feed should be avoided. Compulsory measures to reduce animal stocks are not considered to be a viable alternative.

Methane emissions from cattle feedlots can be reduced by changing the composition of animal feed.

Even if everything was done to optimise manure management, in terms of volumes, storage and application, it would still be useful to impose restrictions on the use of manure in order to attain the emission reduction targets defined.

In the final analysis, it will only be possible to solve the problems associated with the nitrogen budget if animal and plant production is (re-)integrated.

In this context, mention should also be made of the nitrous oxide emissions caused by the use of mineral and organic nitrogen fertiliser. Because of the radiative activity and the ozone-depleting potential of this gas, the use of fertiliser should be further reduced, and it should be geared strictly to the nutrients balances. The aim must be to preserve the nitrogen cycle. This is the only effective way to prevent water, soil and air pollution.

Currently, there is no support for the introduction of a tax on mineral nitrogen fertiliser – either at national level, or at the level of the EC.

5.3.4 Ozone-depleting gases

In the Federal Republic of Germany, most of the legal provisions governing the phase-out of the production and distribution of ozone-depleting gases are laid down in the *FCKW-Halon-Verbots-Verordnung*, the ordinance banning the use of CFCs and halons, which was adopted on 6 May 1991. The substances which are not covered by this ordinance (CFC-111 and CFCs 221 to 217) are subject to the provisions of the European Community, according to which these substances will have to be phased out completely by 1997.

Neither the EC nor the Federal Republic of Germany has adopted any regulation providing for the phase-out of H-CFCs by a certain date (except for H-CFC-22 in the Federal Republic of Germany). Hence, these substances will be subject to the provisions adopted by the parties to the Montreal Protocol at their second meeting in London – as soon as these enter into force. However, even these provisions do not specify any exact, binding deadline; instead, they only include a declaration of intent, according to which 34 H-CFCs are to be phased out by the year 2020.

In the Ordinance on the Ban of CFCs and Halons, which entered into force in the Federal Republic of Germany on 1 August 1991, the timetable for the phase-out of the production and distribution of ozone-depleting substances distinguishes not only between the various compounds involved, but also between their applications. This makes it possible to include the possible substitutes for the various applications. The provisions for the various substances are as follows:

– CFCs can still be used
  – as refrigerants in large mobile plants until early 1994;
  – as refrigerants in small-scale installations until early 1995;

- as foaming agents for insulating material until early 1995.
- H-CFC-22 can be used as a refrigerant, as well as in insulating material and other foamed material until the year 2000. For PUR foams in cans, H-CFC-22 can only be used until early 1993.
- Methyl chloroform can only be used in insulating materials until 1 January 1995.
- The deadlines for the use of carbon tetrachloride and halons have already expired.

Products which contain any of the substances covered by the ordinance banning CFCs and halons must be marked as such (except for insulating materials which contain H-CFC-22). In order to guarantee proper disposal, the distributors of these substances are obliged to take back the products after their use.

The results of NASA's chlorine measurements in the Northern Hemisphere, and similar findings obtained during the European Ozone Research Campaign, have led to increasing political pressure to accelerate the phase-out of ozone-depleting substances. So far, however, no steps have been taken to revise the Ordinance on the Ban on the Use of CFCs and Halons, other than attempts to persuade industry to phase out the substances as early as by the end of 1993 in the framework of voluntary commitments.

The fourth meeting of the parties to the Montreal Protocol will be held in autumn 1992 in Copenhagen. It is too early to say whether another revision of the Protocol will be decided at this meeting in order to introduce more stringent provisions than those applying in the Federal Republic of Germany; and it is also too early to predict when these provisions would enter into force (cf. Chapter 5.1).

References

(1) European Community, 1991, 21+96 et seq.
(2) European Community, Council of the Environment and Energy Ministers, 1991, 1+3
(3) European Community, Commission, 1991, 2
(4) European Community, ECO/Fin Council, 1991, 7 et seq.
(5) European Community, 1991, 75-78
(6) Bundesministerium für Umwelt, Naturschutz und Reaktorsicherheit (Federal Ministry for the Environment, Nature Conservation and Nuclear Safety), 1991, 148 et seq.
(7) European Community, Commission, 1991, 2-11
(8) European Community, 1991, 101 et seq.
(9) European Community, 1992, 44
(10) European Community, 1991, 100
(11) Bundesministerium für Umwelt, Naturschutz und Reaktorsicherheit (Federal Ministry for the Environment, Nature Conservation and Nuclear Safety), 1991, 112 et seq.
(12) Prognos, 1991, 448

6 Recommendations for Action by the International Community of Nations

6.1 Confirmation of the Fundamental Objectives Defined by the Enquete Commission on "Preventive Measures to Protect the Earth's Atmosphere"

The current Enquete Commission emphatically subscribes to the recommendations for CO_2 emission reductions made by the preceding Enquete Commission on "Preventive Measures to Protect the Earth's Atmosphere" in its third report which was submitted in 1990 (cf. Table 6.1) (1).

The reduction targets to be achieved by the year 2005, relative to 1987, can be summarised as follows:

– In the economically strong Western industrialised nations, where per-capita emissions are particularly high at present, CO_2 emissions should be reduced by at least 30 percent.

– In the European Community as a whole, CO_2 emissions should be reduced by at least 20 or 25 percent.

– In the industrialised nations (Western and Eastern industrialised nations taken together), CO_2 emissions should be reduced by at least 20 percent. In this context, it should be borne in mind that targets and predictions will have to be revised to allow for new figures and assessments due to the radical changes that have taken place in the former Eastern bloc countries.

– In the developing countries, the increase in CO_2 emissions should be limited to a maximum of about 50 percent, i.e. annual emission growth rates should be reduced (cf. Fig. 6.1 and Table 6.1).

However, no universal growth rate limit should be applied to all developing countries alike. Instead, a differentiated approach should be adopted vis-à-vis the various countries concerned.

All the reduction targets taken together will lead to a global reduction of CO_2 emissions by at least 5 percent by the year 2005.

Table 6.1: *Targets of the Enquete Commission for the Reduction of Energy-Related CO_2 Emissions by the Year 2005 and by the Year 2050 (percentages relative to the emissions of the respective group of countries in 1987)*

Country group	Percentage reduction targets, relative to the respective emission levels in 1987	
	by 2005 at least	by 2050 at least
Western and Eastern industrialised nations total	−20	−80
Economically strong Western industrialised nations with currently very high per-capita emissions	−30	−80
European Community	−20 to −25	−80
Developing countries	+50	+70
Worldwide	− 5	−50

At first glance, this preliminary reduction target may appear to be rather modest. However, closer scrutiny of the overall impact shows that it represents a global challenge of considerable magnitude:

Between 1987 and 1990, CO_2 emissions already increased by about 7 percent due to increasing energy consumption. This means that global emissions will have to be reduced by as much as 12 percent if the target mentioned above is to be attained (cf. Fig. 6.1).

The envisaged reduction target is tantamount to a reversal of the current trend, which is urgently required if we want to get away from merely reacting to climate change and increasingly take preventive action (cf. Fig. 6.1).

The Enquete Commission "Protecting the Earth's Atmosphere" explicitly subscribes to the fundamental objectives specified in the draft convention prepared by the Enquete Commission on "Preventive Measures to Protect the Earth's Atmosphere" (2).

6.2 Minimum Requirements Recommended for the "United Nations Conference on Environment and Development"

Against the background of the hearing on the status of international political decision-making, which was held by the Enquete Commission "Protecting the Earth's Atmosphere" in January 1992, it cannot be expected that it will be possible to reach a full-scale consensus on all of the fundamental targets mentioned above within a short period of time (3).

It is with this in mind that the Commission has drawn up the recommendations specified below. The Commission feels very strongly that these recommendations are minimum requirements with regard to the outcome of the negotiations which will take place in the next few months.

(1) Our knowledge about man-made climate change has now reached such a high level of certainty that gaps in knowledge can no longer be cited as a reason to refrain from initiating preventive political measures. Wherever governments delay actions designed to reduce emissions of radiatively active substances, this cannot be justified by gaps in knowledge. The international community of nations is called upon:

   – to avert, as much as possible, the threat of climate change,

   – to share in solidarity the adverse effects of the climate change that can no longer be averted.

(2) The need for further research with regard to the foreseeable climate change is not contested. While the current status of scientific knowledge already justifies substantial emission reductions, additional future knowledge may make corresponding action necessary. Current gaps in our knowledge are mainly to be found in the following areas:

   – the accuracy of climate predictions,

   – regional differences in climate change and its impact,

   – the economic as well as the more drastic social effects of climate change in the various countries, in particular with regard to food supply,

   – the effects on the other parts of the biosphere.

The international community of nations is called upon to close the remaining gaps in our knowledge and to take additional action in accordance with new findings.

(3) Most of the currently foreseeable climate change has so far been caused by the industrialised nations. Their current economic system

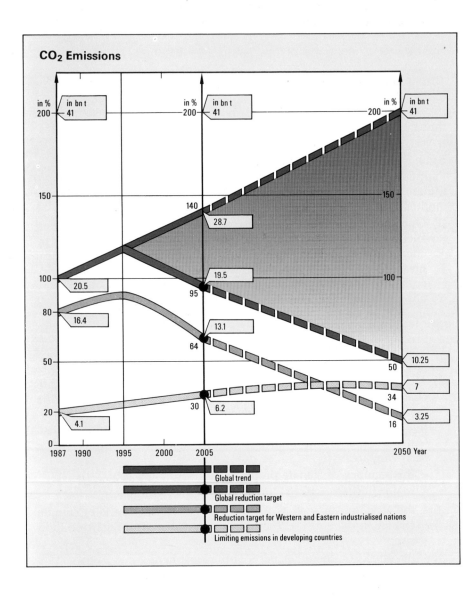

CO₂ Emissions

cannot be applied universally because of its impact on the climate; if it was copied by the developing countries, this would increase the risk of ecological catastrophes. The international community of nations is called upon to identify and implement climatically sound economic systems where it will no longer be possible for any country to benefit at the expense of other countries, future generations or the natural environment. A first step in that direction should be the adoption of the polluter-pays principle (common, but differentiated responsibility) at international level.

(4) It will be above all the Third World countries that will have to suffer from the foreseeable climate change. While climate policy – for the time being – is mainly a task of the industrialised nations because they are the main polluters, the climate crisis must not be aggravated by the future development of countries which are not yet industrialised. Above and beyond current development cooperation, preserving the climatic conditions of life will therefore be a key factor in any future development policy. Poverty must not be perpetuated for the sake of preserving the climate; it will require a new strategy which will have to combine preventive measures to protect the climate with efforts aimed at overcoming poverty. The international community of nations is called upon to search for new policies to be pursued by industrialised nations and developing countries in order to ensure development that is acceptable for all countries in terms of its climatic

---

◄ *Fig. 6.1: Energy-related CO_2 emissions up to the years 2005 and 2050, respectively, based on the reduction plan of the Enquete Commission: Reduction targets for industrialised nations and targets for limiting emission growth rates in developing countries (cf. Tab. 6.1).*

All data are given in billion tonnes and as percentages, relative to total emissions of approx. 20.5 billion in 1987, the baseline year. The curves depicted should not be seen as exact targets as established by means of scenario calculations. Instead, they are merely shown to illustrate the possible effects of the targets envisaged. The breakdown of the sources of global CO_2 emissions between the industrialised nations (accounting for about 80 percent in 1987) and the developing countries (accounting for about 20 percent in 1987) was based on rough estimates. A more differentiated breakdown will have to be determined in the annexes on donor and recipient countries, to be established in the framework of the negotiations on the International Climate and Energy Convention.

N.B.: It has not been possible to modify this figure in order to reflect the radical changes which have taken place in the former Soviet Union.

soundness. These policies must be designed to secure common survival, and they must offer all countries a chance of sustainable development.

(5) This change in the orientation of the global ecological and economic development should be initiated at the "United Nations Conference on Environment and Development". The discrepancies between the industrialised nations and developing countries are so large that only small steps will be possible as long as the industrialised nations consume a disproportionately high share of the goods of the Earth. In the final analysis, however, it is in the interest of all the parties concerned if at least the following steps are taken in Rio de Janeiro for the purpose of vigorously pursuing the process aimed at developing an effective international climate policy.

(a) The international community of nations should agree immediately after the Conference to enter into negotiations on a protocol designed to lay down specific reduction targets for emissions of radiatively active substances.

(b) The protocol to be adopted at the end of these negotiations should be based on the current status of scientific findings.

(c) The protocol should be reviewed in previously defined intervals and amended accordingly in order to reflect the progress in climate change and in scientific findings.

(d) All the climatically relevant scientific research findings that are accessible to the countries which are parties to the protocol should immediately be evaluated and made available internationally.

(6) The global objective set by the 1988 Toronto Climate Conference was to reduce global emissions of radiatively active substances by 20 percent by the year 2005 and by 50 percent by the middle of the next century. The validity of these targets has been clearly confirmed by recent findings. The international community of nations is called upon generally to confirm the objective defined in Toronto, irrespective of what reduction rates will be allocated to specific countries.

(7) The conference in Rio de Janeiro should already lead to concrete agreements reflecting the immediate political will of all the countries represented to take seriously measures designed to protect the climate. In accordance with the polluter-pays principle, it is primarily the industrialised nations which are called upon to initiate concrete steps to introduce an effective global climate policy. The developing countries will be unable to make their contributions without support from industrialised nations; in fact, they will need both technological and financial assistance.

In Rio de Janeiro, it will be necessary to conclude agreements which set out the required new approaches towards cooperation and towards accomodating the conflicting interests of the industrialised nations and of the developing countries, and which form a platform for common action. In view of the urgency of this matter, the participants in Rio de Janeiro should not content themselves with adopting general and incomprehensible declarations. Instead, they should agree on ways of immediately initiating the institutional, financial and technological cooperation which will be needed in future between the industrialised nations and the developing countries, thereby facilitating subsequent negotiations on a climate convention.

– For this purpose, the international community of nations is called upon – as far as institutional cooperation is concerned – from now on to accept the Global Environmental Facility (GEF) not only as a pilot concept but as a permanent institution. The decision-making structure of the GEF will have to changed in such a way that it will be acceptable for all countries, including the developing countries; hence, in terms of its substance and the procedure adopted, it can set an example for a novel type of environmental partnership. In this context, the experience with the Multilateral Fund of the Montreal Protocol should serve as a model.

– In the field of financial cooperation, the industrialised nations are called upon to make substantial increases in their contributions to the GEF – at least by a factor of 3 – up to the entry into force of a climate convention. The funds to be made available for this purpose should not be obtained by reducing other environmental expenditure. The German Federal Government is called upon to declare its readiness to adopt such an approach jointly with all the other industrialised nations.

The Commission proposes that a limited so-called "Green Fund" (climate fund) should be established to supplement the GEF. This "Green Fund" should be used to finance all those environmental projects which, under the current agreements, are covered by neither the GEF nor the Multilateral Fund of the Montreal Protocol.

- In order to initiate and promote the process of technological cooperation between the North and the South as early as at the conference in Rio de Janeiro, it would be desirable to reach preliminary agreements in this field, as well. These agreements should include the following points:

(a) Upon the request of developing countries, the resources of the GEF should be used to promote studies aimed at describing and defining the potential future contributions of specific countries and regions in the South towards a global climate policy. These studies should be carefully conducted in cooperation between the country concerned, the GEF and external experts. It is essential that these studies should address not only the technological capacities that are present now and needed in future; instead, they should also deal with human resources issues such as training, know-how and management.

(b) At the same time, the GEF should draw up inventories of the latest technologies which can contribute towards reducing greenhouse gas emissions in the various countries and regions concerned, in as cost-effective a manner as possible.

(c) On the basis of the country reports and the inventory list to be drawn up, the countries represented in the GEF should decide which technologies should be promoted in the various countries and regions; in this context, cost/benefit ratio considerations should play the key role.

Conceivable instruments of implementation at national and international level – such as taxes, levies, voluntary restraint commitments, as well as cooperation and compensation instruments (joint implementation) – whose usefulness will have yet to be established, should be applied if they support the objectives of the convention. Where necessary, the rules of GATT and of the World Bank should be adapted to this regime.

(8) The common objective of preventing catastrophic global climate change can only be attained if individual countries demonstrate on their own initiative that this objective can be achieved and how it can be achieved. The Federal Republic of Germany has undertaken to reduce CO_2 emissions by at least 25 percent (relative to 1987 levels) by the year 2005. Other countries are following suit. The international community of nations should call upon all countries possessing the necessary economic, technological and political prerequisites not to wait for the adoption of a climate convention and its implementation protocols; instead, they should immediately start preparing and implementing effective national and regional measures designed to protect the climate.

6.3 Other Recommendations

In order to implement the commitments made at national level, the Enquete Commission "Protecting the Earth's Atmosphere" recommends to the German Bundestag and to the German Federal Government that they should support the introduction of a split energy/CO_2 tax as proposed by the Commission of the European Communities, and that they should examine the other instruments aimed at reducing CO_2 emissions which are mentioned in Annex 1.

In addition, the Enquete Commission recommends that the following projects, which are described in more detail in Annex 2 and which are examples of the cooperation suggested in the fields of science and technology, should be supported:

(1) a central monitoring station as a contribution to global environmental monitoring in the framework of the Global Atmosphere Watch (GAW) network;

(2) a political initiative aimed at building a solar thermal power station in the Earth's sun belt;

(3) a political initiative aimed at reducing methane and CO_2 emissions from the gas pipeline system of the former Soviet Union.

References

(1) Third Report of the Enquete Commission on "Preventive Measures to Protect the Earth's Atmosphere", 1990, vol. 2, p. 867
(2) Ibid., p. 848 ff
(3) Commission document no. 12/3

Instruments for Reducing CO_2 Emissions

1. Objectives and Opportunities

The Federal Republic of Germany has set itself the target of reducing CO_2 emissions by between 25 and 30 percent by the year 2005. This target goes beyond the general trend in CO_2 reductions. In addition, the Federal Republic of Germany also intends to activate reduction potentials at international level.

Generally speaking, there are five sets of instruments to choose from:

1. Conventional energy and environmental policy instruments.
2. A quota system to limit CO_2 emissions, i.e. imposing quantitative restrictions, which might be linked to a scheme of tradeable permits.
3. A general tax or levy, imposed either on emissions or on energy consumption.
4. Voluntary restraint commitments on the part of industry to reduce emissions of radiatively active trace gases, both domestically and by way of cooperation in other countries.
5. Transnational cooperation designed to reduce CO_2 emissions and permit joint implementation.

The assessment of these policy instruments in terms of their feasibility and implementability – both in the Federal Republic of Germany and internationally – should be completed by a specified date (1993-94).

2. Conventional Energy and Environmental Policy Instruments

In attempting to reduce CO_2 emissions, the Federal Republic of Germany has concentrated its efforts on the spectrum of conventional energy and environmental policy instruments – as have all the other countries around the world. These interventions are designed to conserve energy, encourage the substitution of low-CO_2 fuels for high-CO_2 energy sources, promote the development of renewable energy sources and – in some countries – the use of nuclear energy. This can be achieved by applying measures which affect prices or costs, or which restrict volumes. The list of possible measures is quite long, including restrictions imposed on uses, quantitative restrictions for fossil fuels, emission ceilings, subsidies, and taxes. A number of specific regulations and measures have been adopted to deal with the transport sector.

By means of these instruments, it has been possible to achieve substantial emission reductions everywhere, and this will continue in future. However, these instruments alone will not suffice to attain the targets defined in 1988 by the Toronto Climate Conference. For this reason, other measures have to be considered, as well.

3. An Energy/CO_2 Tax, i.e. a General Tax Imposed on CO_2 Emissions and Energy Consumption

Energy/CO_2 taxes can have two effects: they can encourage energy conservation, and they can lead to the replacement of one energy source by another.

The Enquete Commission "Protecting the Earth's Atmosphere" supports the initiative of the Commission of the European Communities for the introduction of a "split" energy/CO_2 tax, based on the following criteria:

- The tax should be applied at least in all the Member States of the European Community.
- If the tax is introduced only at national level, it must be ensured that this will not lead to distortion of competition within the Common Market. It must be guaranteed that the expenses involved in restructuring the energy system are within the scope of the revenue obtained.
- The social acceptability of the tax must be guaranteed.
- There must be no discrimination.

4. Quantitative Restrictions, Permits

The regulatory measures described above and the energy/CO_2 tax may be sufficient to attain the reduction target envisaged. However, if this is not the case, quantitative restrictions should be imposed on CO_2 emissions. In order to optimise the effectiveness of such a measure, it would be necessary to introduce a system of tradeable permits.

5. Transnational Cooperation Designed to Reduce CO_2 Emissions and to Permit Joint Implementation

The measures mentioned so far only affect national CO_2 emissions. However, the potential for reducing CO_2 emissions on a global scale is far more significant. In order to make use of international reduction potentials as well, a fifth instrument should be added to the four traditional policy instruments described above, i.e. transnational cooperation between companies, with the aim of reducing CO_2 emissions.

Joint implementation: In order to facilitate the attainment of national – as well as future international – reduction targets (e.g. by transnational cooperation), companies should have the option – following a favourable review – of participating in joint implementation. In this context, it will be necessary to define the reduction rate to be achieved domestically and the reduction share to be contributed on the basis of a reduction commitment with the respective partner. These instruments should be included in the current negotiations on a climate convention, and their compatibility with GATT should also be guaranteed. International compensation of reduction commitments can make sense if it makes it possible to reach the common goal of reducing global CO_2 emissions earlier than by strictly national measures. However, such arrangements must not lead to one-sided advantages with regard to existing commitments.

The question as to how transnational cooperation agreements should be designed and how this system can be harmonised with the traditional instruments described above will have to be examined by the Enquete Commission "Protecting the Earth's Atmosphere" in future.

Examples of International Scientific and Technological Cooperation

1. Proposal for the Establishment and the Operation of a Central Monitoring Station in the Framework of Global Environmental Monitoring

The Enquete Commission "Protecting the Earth's Atmosphere" supports the initiative of WMO (World Meteorological Organisation) aimed at establishing a Global Atmosphere Watch (GAW), i.e. a global environmental monitoring network into which the two current systems – GOOS (Global Ozone Observing System) and BAPMON (Background Air Pollution Monitoring Network) – should be integrated. GAW will be used as an early warning system which will help to detect – in time – changes in the troposphere's chemical composition, the stratospheric ozone layer, as well as in the regional and global transport, and in the chemistry, of environmentally relevant trace gases. In addition, GAW will help to monitor compliance with international protocols and conventions such as the Montreal Protocol.

In addition, the data collected in GAW will be used to improve our understanding of the chemical behaviour of the atmosphere and of its interactions with the biosphere and the oceans. This will make it possible to predict future changes in the chemical composition of the atmosphere due to human activities, and their effects on the environment. These predictions can then be used as a basis to define suitable, cost-effective measures designed to minimise or prevent environmental problems.

In preparation of the United Nations Conference on Environment and Development, the Enquete Commission recommends to the German Bundestag and to the German Federal Government that the Federal Republic of Germany should participate in the international environmental monitoring network GAW by building and operating a GAW station, and that this station should be introduced as a contribution of the Federal Republic of Germany in the international negotiations on a climate convention. The Enquete Commission suggests that the "Schneefernerhaus" located on the Zugspitze mountain at an altitude of 2,650 meters should be converted into a "High-Altitude Environmental Observatory". This observatory should be combined with the attached GAW Regional Resource Center for Quality Assurance to form a "Central GAW Station Zugspitze" to be integrated into the global environmental monitoring network.

By accepting the responsibilities associated with such a station, the Federal Republic of Germany would play a leading role within the GAW network and make an important contribution towards the promotion of atmospheric sciences in developing countries by supervising the GAW stations located in these countries and by training the scientists and engineers employed at these stations.

2. Political Initiative for the Construction of a Thermal-Type Solar Power Station in the Earth's Sun Belt

Against the background of what has been achieved in almost 20 years of research, development and demonstration, and in preparation of the United Nations Conference on Environment and Development, the Enquete Commission "Protecting the Earth's Atmosphere" recommends to the German Bundestag and to the German Federal Government that, as a significant contribution to the conference, the Federal Republic of Germany should agree with other industrialised nations and a suitable developing country to build a thermal-type solar power station in the sun belt of the Earth (cf. (1)).

For several years now, commercial 350 MW_{el} thermal-type solar power stations have been reliably operating in California in a hybrid mode (solar plus fossil). Their availability is comparable to that of conventional power stations, and they are ready to be marketed worldwide.

An 80 MW_{el} parabolic troughs power station with supplementary fossil fuel use currently costs about DM 380 million. The manufacturers expect the costs to decrease to about DM 280 million as a result of further technological improvements and if more power stations are built.

Interest and the repayment of the investment costs account for a major portion (70 percent) of the electricity generation costs of about DM 0.26/kWh_{el}, which has been averaged over 20 years and is based on the assumption that fuel prices will increase by 4 percent annually. If a coal-fired power station was used for the same purpose, i.e. a power station which only uses fossil fuels, the electricity generation costs would amount to about DM 0.20/kWh_{el}. While the investment costs of a coal-fired power plant are only about half of the investments needed for a solar power station, the fuel costs during the operation of the plant are four times higher than those of a solar power station.

In both cases, the electricity generation costs would be about equal if a non-repayable contribution amounting to about 30 percent of the investment costs, i.e. DM 115 million, was granted by the industrialised nations. In this case, no subsidies would be required during the 20-year period of operation. A solar power station can help to reduce the amount of foreign exchange spent to pay for fossil fuels, in particular for countries which depend on energy imports. If the solar power station was operated for more than 20 years (30 years are common), it would generate an additional profit because there would be no more capital costs, and because of the lower fuel demand, the operating costs would be much lower than those of exclusively fossil-fueled power stations.

The annual CO_2 emissions of a solar power station which uses 25 percent fossil fuels are 155,000 tonnes lower than those of a coal-fired power station and 135,000 tonnes below those of an oil-fired power station, which adds up to 3.1 million and 2.7 million tonnes, respectively, over a period of 20 years, and more than 4 million tonnes over a period of 30 years.

All the costs very much depend on the specific conditions prevailing at the location selected and on the particular terms of financing. Hence, precise figures can only be determined for a concrete project. Concrete plans exist for Brazil and India. The key criteria for choosing a partner country will be whether the country concerned generally pursues a policy aimed at conserving energy, whether it is directly interested in solar power stations, and whether this country is prepared to play an active role with regard to the financing, the construction and the operation of the power plant.

The Enquete Commission "Protecting the Earth's Atmosphere" recommends to the German Bundestag and to the German Federal Government that the Federal Republic of Germany should take the initiative for the construction of a first exemplary solar power station in the near future, and that the Federal Republic of Germany should make a significant contribution to the financing of this project. If one takes into account the non-repayable contribution, the costs of this solar power station for the country operating it will be about at the same level as the costs of a conventional power station. During its period of operation, there will be no need for subsidies. This power station will be independent of the imponderabilities of the energy resources market.

An aspect which is considered to be particularly important is the fact that this first step would mark the beginning of a long-term programme for the construction of solar power stations. Only if this happens can industry be expected to show the commitment needed to build up a self-supporting solar energy industry. Increasingly, solar power station components could also be manufactured in developing and newly industrialised countries.

3. Political Initiative for the Reduction of Methane and Carbon Dioxide Emissions from the Gas Transport System of the Former Soviet Union

At the hearing held by the Enquete Commission "Protecting the Earth's Atmosphere" in order to establish the status of scientific findings on the greenhouse effect, the problem of methane emissions from the gas industry was once again discussed. Based on current findings, it is assumed that any actions taken to reduce gas leakages from old pipeline systems will be highly efficient in terms of reducing greenhouse gas emissions in a cost-effective manner.

According to conservative estimates, about 8 percent of the gas transported is lost each year during its production and supraregional distribution on the territory of the former Soviet Union. These losses are due to leakages and insufficient compressor efficiency. The length of the long-distance pipeline network is 220,000 kilometers. The losses correspond to about 40 billion cubic meters of gas, and hence, are equivalent to about half of the annual gas consumption volume in the Federal Republic of Germany.

About one-third of the losses occur occur in the compressor stations which are responsible for the transport of the gas. At these stations, burnt gas is released into the atmosphere in the form of carbon dioxide. The remainder of the losses – i.e. more than half – reaches the atmosphere in the form of methane because of the substances that natural gas is composed of. Since the global warming potential of methane is substantially higher than that of carbon dioxide, the leakages described considerably exacerbate the climate problem. In this calculation, the losses which occur during the regional distribution (another 250,000 kilometers of pipelines) and on the premises of the final consumers have not even been taken into account.

The state of the art of modern gas pipelines, which are overwhelmingly used in Western Europe and North America, makes it possible to keep methane losses below 0.5 percent of the gas volume transported.

According to preliminary estimates, it can be assumed that the additional revenue which would be earned if the pipelines and compressor stations were modernised would be higher than the expenditure required.

For the reasons mentioned above, there is an urgent need for action. Consequently, the Enquete Commission "Protecting the Earth's Atmosphere" recommends to the German Bundestag and to the German Federal Government that the Federal Republic of Germany should initiate transnational cooperation with the governmental agencies in charge in the former Soviet Union and that this cooperation should be embedded in intergovernmental agreements and promoted as a high-priority political objective.

References

---

(1) Forum für Zukunftsenergien, 1992

Glossary

absorption of radiation
Uptake of radiative energy by a solid body, a liquid or a gas; the energy absorbed is then transformed into another form of energy (usually heat).

aerosol
Solid or liquid particles (other than water or ice particles) in the air, ranging between 0.1 and 100 μm in size.

agroforestry
Cultivation of trees in plantations integrated into a farming system, where the trees are used for the production of timber and other forestry products, or a management system of ecologically, technologically and economically sustainable, integrated cultivation of trees and agricultural crop plants or pastures.

air pollutants
Substances found in the air which have either direct or indirect harmful effects on the biosphere, e.g. nitrogen oxides, sulphur dioxide, volatile organic compounds and ozone.

albedo (reflectivity)
A measure of the reflecting power of a given surface, expressed as the ratio of reflected radiation to total solar radiation for a certain wavelength or spectral range (The reflecting surface may be the ocean surface, snow or the Earth/atmosphere system as a whole).

anaerobic
Characterised by the absence of air, e.g. in water.

anthropogenic [Greek ánthrópos = man, and Greek genés = to produce, to create]
Resulting from, or influenced by, human activities.

arid
A dry climate with less than three months of rainfall per year.

190

atmosphere [Greek atmós = vapour, steam and Greek sphaîra = sphere, globe]
The gaseous layer surrounding a planet, in particular the Earth. The Earth's atmosphere can be broken down according to mean vertical temperature distribution into the following layers: The troposphere is the lower part of the atmosphere, which is mainly responsible for meteorological conditions. The upper limit of the troposphere is the tropopause, which extends from 8 to 17 km in altitude. The stratosphere consists of strata extending from the tropopause to the stratopause at an altitude of approx. 50 km. The ozone layer lies within the stratosphere. The Earth,s atmosphere is mainly composed of nitrogen, oxygen, argon, water vapour and carbon dioxide.

atmospheric radiation window
A region of infrared radiation where atmospheric water vapour absorbs little radiation, so that almost all of the long-wave radiation emitted (reflected) from the Earth's surface can reach space. Many → greenhouse gases absorb more infrared radiation in this region, so that increases in the concentrations of greenhouse gases lead to an additional warming of the atmosphere.

biomass
The total dry weight of the living organisms of a single species or all species in a community or stand, measured at a given point in time. Biomass comprises plant biomass (phytomass) and animal biomass (zoomass). The mass of dead and cast-off plant components is often additionally measured and referred to as "dead" biomass.

biosphere
The part of the Earth which is filled with life and which is able to support life, i.e. the envelope of the geosphere (Earth) and the lower atmosphere (air) with all living organisms.

biota
→ biosphere.

boreal
Of, or relating to, northern geographic regions; the climate of northern Europe, Asia, and North America.

carbohydrates
Important reserve substances of plants with characterstic chemical properties. Carbohydrates include starch, glucose and fructose.

carbon cycle
The cycle of carbon in its various chemical compounds between the → atmosphere, the → biosphere, the hydrosphere and the → lithosphere.

carbon dioxide (CO₂)

Colourless, non-flammable, slightly acidic gas. In the presence of solar energy and water, CO_2 is metabolised by plants and transformed into carbohydrates. When plants or → fossil fuels formed from plant material are burnt, the carbon they contain is once again released as CO_2. Carbon dioxide is an important → greenhouse gas, whose atmospheric concentration currently amounts to 355 ppm.

catalyst

A substance which influences a chemical reaction, but which itself undergoes no change in the process. Chlorine atoms and chlorine oxide radicals act as catalysts during stratospheric ozone depletion, i.e. they are capable of splitting a large number of ozone molecules before they themselves are consumed by other chemical reactions.

cataract

Opacity of the lens of the eye.

ceteris paribus

All other things being equal; analysis of the cause/effect relationship between specific exogenous and endogenous variables while all other exogeneous variables remain constant.

chlorofluorocarbons (CFCs)

Industrially produced organic halogen compounds. Until a few years ago, CFCs were mainly used as propellants in aerosols. Today, they are mainly applied as blowing agents in plastics production, as cleaners and solvents, and as refrigerants. Direct exposure to CFCs does not cause any noxious effects; in the → stratosphere, however, they are broken down by radiation, thus leading to the formation of the → ozone hole above Antarctica. CFCs also enhance the → greenhouse effect.

There are two types of chlorofluorocarbon: fully halogenated and partially halogenated CFCs. Fully halogenated CFCs are composed exclusively of carbon and → halogens, and have high → ozone-depleting potentials. Several fully halogenated compounds are not listed in the → Montreal Protocol (e.g. carbon tetrachloride (CCL_4)). Partially halogenated CFCs also contain hydrogen atoms, and hence, are chemically less stable. Partially halogenated CFCs such as H-CFC-22 are now being considered as substitutes for fully halogenated CFCs. However, several partially halogenated CFCs also add to the greenhouse effect, and contribute to the destruction of the ozone layer — albeit to a lesser degree.

circulation model

A type of climate model.

climate
The atmospheric conditions characteristic of a particular location over a long period of time, usually more than 30 years.

climate model
Description of the → climate by means of a mathematical physical computer model.

climate parameter
Internal climate parameters are physical variables which directly characterise the climate, such as radiation, temperature and precipitation. External climate parameter, on the other hand, are variables which influence the climate system but do not interact with it (e.g. solar radiation, volcanoes, and man-made emissions of greenhouse gases).

climate variability
Short-term changes in climate.

co-generation
The combined generation of electricity and heat or process heat, which permits high utilisation of the primary energy used.

collectible energy
→ used energy.

combined heat and power (CHP)
→ co-generation.

CO_2 fertilising effect
Increased plant growth due to higher atmospheric CO_2 concentrations.

condensation
The transition from the vapour phase to the liquid phase. In meteorology: when atmospheric water vapour changes into a liquid state, forming droplets in the process (clouds, fog, dew).

condensation nuclei
Airborne particles to which water vapour tends to attach.

concentrations of trace gases
In this report, the volumetric → mixing ratios of trace gases are referred to as concentrations, which is common practice in atmospheric physics.

convection
Ascent of air masses, often limited to small areas.

cost/benefit analysis
An instrument used to support governmental decision-making: the decision-making process is made more transparent by means of systematically and, where possible, comprehensively analysing all the costs and benefits involved in specific actions, and by providing an overall assessment.

Crash
A CO_2 study conducted by the European Community which focused on the following three areas
- cost efficiency analyses of CO_2 reduction potentials
- effects of energy and CO_2 taxes on CO_2 emissions
- analysis of the effects of various taxation models in the energy sector.

cyclone
A depression; low-pressure system.

degradation
Changes in the biomass density of forests, or in typical soil profiles caused by human interventions, or by changes in climate, vegetation cover, or soil populations. Degradation is often accompanied by a decline in soil fertility.

delivered energy
$\rightarrow$ end-point energy

denitrification
The process by which microbes reduce nitrates (NO_3) to atmospheric nitrogen (N_2) or to nitrous oxide (N_2O).

deposition
The process of depositing on surfaces.

discount factor
Indicator used by the current generation to assess future costs and benefits.

EC Commission
The Commission of the $\rightarrow$ European Communities (based in Brussels) watches over the correct application of the provisions of the European Treaties; it drafts proposals for decisions to be made by the EC Council on the development of Community policies, and it is the executive organ responsible for implementing Community policies on the basis of Council desisions, or directly applying provisions of the European Treaties.

There are 14 Commissioners of equal standing, of which 2 each are appointed by the larger EC Member States (Federal Republic of Germany, France, the United

194

Kingdom and Italy), while the other Member States appoint one Commissioner each. The Commission members, who are appointed by their respective governments in mutual agreement, are completely independent of national governments in their work. The Commission operates in accordance with the collegial principle; decisions are adopted on the basis of simple majorities.

ecosystem
The combination between a plant and animal community (biocoenosis) and its habitat (biotope).

El Niño event
The intense and prolonged warming of the ocean surface off the coast of Peru and along the equatorial Pacific, which occurs at irregular intervals every few years.

emission of trace gases
The release of → trace gases from a reservoir in the atmosphere.

end-point energy
End-point energy is the energy available to the final consumer. As a rule, this includes most → secondary energy sources, e. g. coal, oil and gas products, electricity and district heating, but also directly usable → primary energy sources such as natural gas. Losses involved in the conversion of primary energy into end-point energy (particularly in generating electricity), together with the portion of primary energy not used for energy purposes, currently amount to one-third of the primary energy used in the Federal Republic of Germany. This means that only about two-thirds of the country's primary energy is available as end-point energy.

energy conservation/energy services
In the present report, energy conservation is always seen in the context of an energy service concept, i. e. various services (heating, light, power) are aimed at satisfying the so-called energy demand. This demand has always been satisfied through a combination of factors such as energy, capital and technological know-how. The optimum combination of these factors depends on the relative costs involved. In view of increasing energy prices, as well as the external costs of various energy conversion processes, it will make sound environmental and economic sense in future to replace energy to a large extent by investments and technological know-how. Energy conservation thus means guaranteeing the same energy services as before, but with a more efficient combination of the various factors involved. The entire field of energy must be kept in mind when defining energy conservation, i.e. a reduction in energy turnover will only have been achieved when this reduction also applies to the primary energy balance. "Energy conservation" is used as a generic term in this context. It involves the

minimisation of energy use for a given level of energy services over the entire energy process chain, i.e. including the conversion of → primary energy into end-point energy, and the conversion of end-point energy into → used energy, or the energy service itself. Questions of supply and demand should be taken into consideration when deciding on energy conservation measures.

energy conservation potentials
It is common practice to distinguish between four different types of energy potential:
- The theoretical potential is the sum of energy sources and energy conservation, calculated on the basis of physical or scientific laws.
- The technical potential is derived from the theoretical potential, taking into consideration the efficiency of the various systems that are used to tap energy sources, or to conserve energy, as well as other relevant technical aspects. By definition, the technical potential represents state-of-the-art technology.
- The economic potential restricts the technical potential to that part which is economically competitive compared to the costs of corupeting systems.
- The expected potential is that portion of the economic potential which takes into consideration the speed of market introduction and other factors, and hence is the utilised economic potential to be expected within a given general economic setting.

energy-related emissions of radiatively active trace gases
→ Trace gases which are released during the generation, conversion, distribution and use of energy, and which directly or indirectly cause climate change. These trace gases include:
- carbon dioxide (CO_2),
- methane (CH_4),
- nitrous oxide (laughing gas, N_2O),
- trace gases which contribute to the formation of tropospheric ozone (O_3), or which cause chemical changes in the air, in particular nitrogen oxides (NO_x), carbon monoxide (CO), hydrocarbons (C_xH_y), and sulphur dioxide (SO_2),
- other trace gases which require further in-depth study as regards their impact on the climate.

energy services
→ Energy conservation/energy services.

energy units and energy conversion factors
The standard unit for measuring energy is the joule (SI). It has been the official unit of measurement in Germany since 1 January 1978. By law, the calorie (cal) and other units derived from it — coal equivalents (CE) and crude oil equivalents (1 CE = 0.7 COE) — can be used as supplementary units of

measurement for a transitional period only. One joule (J) = 1 newton meter (Nm) = 1 watt-second (Ws).

The following energy units are commonly used:
1 terawatt-hour = 1 tWh = 1 x 10^9 kWh = 3.6 PJ = 0.123 mn t CE;
1 million tonnes of coal equivalents = 1 mn t CE = 29.308 PJ = 8.15 tWh;
1 exajoule = 1 EJ = 278 tWh

Conversion factors:

	kJ	kWh	kg CE
1 kJ	–	0.000278	0.000034
1 kWh	3,600	–	0,123
1 kg CE	29,308	8.14	–

erosion
→ soil erosion

erosion of the gene pool
Loss of genetic material, for example, due to the extinction of terrestrial varieties for various staple foods.

estuary
A funnel-shaped inlet of sea at the mouth of a river.

European Communities
The term "European Communities" is used to refer to three separate organisations
– the European Coal and Steel Community (ECSC, Coal and Steel Pool)
– the European Economic Community (EEC)
– the European Atomic Energy Community (Euratom)

The use of the term "European Community" to refer to all three is political and not legal in nature.

eutrophication
Over-fertilisation, i.e. excessive application of nitrate and phosphate-based nutrients.

evapotranspiration
Evaporation of water vapour from living organisms (→ transpiration) and non-living surfaces (evaporation).

external effects
Effects which the actions of a given economic unit (enterprises, households, etc.) have on another unit, and which are not compensated in any way by the market.

fauna
Animal life.

flora
Plant life.

fossil fuels
Solid, liquid and gaseous fuels such as coal, oil and gas, which have developed from the remains of plants of past geological ages.

GATT
→ General Agreement on Tariffs and Trade.

General Agreement on Tariffs and Trade (GATT)
A multinational treaty concluded within the scope of the United Nations with the goal of removing obstacles to international trade. GATT entered into force on 1 January 1948. Currently, 96 countries are full members of GATT (the Federal Republic of Germany joined in 1951); one country (Tunisia) is a provisional member, and 28 countries apply the Agreement as a matter of fact.

The General Agreement on Tariffs and Trade is based on the following major principles: Trade between countries is to take place on the basis of non-discrimination. In particular, all the parties to the Agreement are obliged to apply the most-favoured-nation principle when they impose import and export duties and corresponding levies. Domestic industries can be protected by tariffs only. Quotas and other non-tariff trade barriers are generally prohibited. They can be applied only in certain exceptional cases (e.g. to protect a country's balance of payments). Disputes must be settled in accordance with the procedure laid down in the Agreement.

GATT's main role has been that of a forum for international negotiations on the reduction of trade barriers.

general equilibrium-response models
Theoretic economic models used to analyse system interrelationships; the first key question is whether or not an equilibrium develops in a given model (multiple equilibria are not precluded); and, if so, which kind of an equilibrium, and whether this equilibrium is stable; secondly, welfare effects can also be analysed within the framework of this model; general equilibrium-response models can be used both for a purely descriptive analysis of system interrelationships and for an assessment of political measures.

greenhouse effect
The greenhouse effect is caused by atmospheric gases which allow short-wave solar radiation to reach the Earth's surface almost unhindered, while they

absorb a large part of the long-wave heat radiation from the Earth's surface and from the atmosphere. Owing to the heat insulating effect of these trace gases, the surface temperature is about 30 °C higher than the radiative temperature of the Earth/atmosphere system without these gases (natural greenhouse effect). Man-made increases in trace gas concentrations are expected to provoke an enhanced greenhouse effect – also referred to as the man-made greenhouse effect – and a temperature rise.

greenhouse gas
Atmospheric gases involved in the → greenhouse effect (water vapour, CO_2, N_2O, CH_4, O_3, CFCs).

halogens (Greek "salt formers")
The five non-metallic elements, i.e. fluorine (F), chlorine (Cl), bromine (Br), iodine (J) and astatine (At).

halons
Halons are brominated → chlorofluorocarbons with extremely high → ozone-depleting potentials. Halons are mainly used as fire extinguishing agents. However, only about 6 percent of the halons are actually used to extinguish fires, while the largest portion remains in fire extinguishing devices and systems, and the remainder is released into the atmosphere during fire drills, during filling operations and as a result of accidental releases (→ Montreal Protocol).

heat of condensation
Heat which is released during the transition from the gaseous to the liquid state of aggregation.

HERMES
Harmonised European Research on Models of Energy Systems.

hydrocarbons
Organic compounds which consist of carbon and hydrogen. When other elements such as → halogens are added, hydrocarbons can be transformed into halogenated hydrocarbons.

hydrological cycle
Water cycle.

inclination of the Earth's axis
The tilt of the Earth's rotational axis from the plane of its orbit around the sun.

inner-tropical convergence zone
The zone, located between the trade wind systems of the two hemispheres, where air masses rise. There are frequent showers and thunderstorms in this zone.

interglacial
Time periods in the Earth's climatological history when the mean surface temperature of the Earth was relatively high.

internalisation of external effects
Inclusion of → external effects in the price mechanism, thereby ensuring that the economic unit causing the external effects will have to bear the full burden of the consequences of its actions.

inversion
In meteorology, reversal of the lapse rate in the troposphere, i.e. temperatures begin to increase with increasing altitudes.

leguminosae
Legumes or pulses; herbaceous plants or trees which produce legumes. They live in symbiosis with nitrogen-fixing nodule bacteria. Several economically important crop plants belong to the leguminosae, including beans, peas, clover, alfalfa, groundnuts and soybeans.

lifetime
The mean residence time of gases in the atmosphere.

lithosphere
The outer, rock Stratum of the Earth.

long-wave spectral range
The range of electromagnetic radiation between 4 and 100 μm.

macroeconomics
Analysis of the interrelationship between overall economic variables (unemployment rate, price level, savings ratio, etc.).

meridional
Parallel to the circles of longitude.

methanogenic archaeobacteria, methanotrophic bacteria
Methanogenic archaeobacteria are primitive bacteria which developed early during the evolutionary process and which can produce methane in the absence

of oxygen. Methanotropic bacteria are able to consume methane, transforming it into CO_2 in the process.

MIDAS
Medium-Term Integrated Demand and Supply Energy System.

mixing ratio
In atmospheric research, it has become standard practice to quote the concentrations of trace elements as mixing ratios (= molar fractions). The volumetric mixing ratio is defined as the ratio of the number of molecules of the gas involved to the sum-total of all molecules. The following abbreviations are commonly used:

1 ppmv (one part per million per volume): 10^{-6}
1 ppbv (one part per billion per volume): 10^{-9}
1 pptv (one part per trillion per volume): 10^{-12}

modal split
Economically efficient distribution of passenger and freight transport among the various modes of transport (road, rail, air, water).

models
One-dimensional (1-d) models: Models used to calculate the total column density and the vertical distribution of trace gases.
Two-dimensional (2-d) models: Models using latitude in addition to altitude in order to allow for latitude-dependent solar radiation.
Three-dimensional (3-d) models: Models including longitude as a third dimension; as far as chemical issues are concerned, 3-d models are still at an early stage of development.

monetarisation
Assessment in terms of monetary units.

Montreal Protocol
The Montreal Protocol on Substances that Deplete the → Ozone Layer was adopted on 16 September 1987 and entered into force on 1 January 1989. The Montreal Protocol, which is the first follow-up agreement to the → Vienna Convention, is a cornerstone of environmental policy. The Protocol controls the production and consumption of the most important fully halogenated → CFCs, and of certain → halons.
The terms of the Protocol were strengthened at the second meeting of the parties to the Montreal Protocol, which was held in London in June 1990.

multilateral fund
Fund established at the second meeting of the Parties to the Montreal Protocol designed to help developing countries phase out substances which deplete the ozone layer by providing financial aid.

mutagenic effect
A non-specific effect which induces genetic mutation.

mycorrhiza
A symbiosis between fungi and higher plants. The root tips of trees, are enveloped by a thick mantle of fungi. Assimilates are extracted from the host, while the fungi assume the function of supplying water and ions to their host trees.

net primary production
The net flux of carbon from the atmosphere to green plants. It is composed of the gross flux of carbon to green plants (the carbon being sequestered in the plants by means of → photosynthesis) less CO_2 → respiration by the plants.

neutrality of revenue
A term from the theory of public finance: when a government earns revenue by using a given instrument (e.g. a tax), and this revenue is designed to finance another measure (e.g. a subsidy).

nitrification
The conversion of nitrogen by microbes, during which first nitrites (NO_2), and then nitrates (NO_3) are formed from ammonia (NH_4).

nitrogen oxides (NO_x)
NO_x is released into the atmosphere almost exclusively as NO. Since a photochemical equilibrium between NO and NO_2 tends to establish itself very quickly, the term generally used is NO_x, representing the sum of NO and NO_2. NO_x develops during high-temperature combustion processes, particularly in motor vehicles and power plants.

North/South dialogue
A term used to describe all the efforts made to reconcile the interests of the industrialised nations and the developing countries.

orbital parameters
The parameters which describe the Earth's orbit, such as the → precession of the orbital perihelion, the → inclination of the Earth's axis, as well as the → eccentricity of the Earth's orbit.

ozone (Greek "odour")

Molecule composed of three oxygen atoms; chemical symbol: O_3. Most atmospheric ozone is found in the stratosphere at an altitude of between 12 and 40 km, where it is generated by means of photodissociation of oxygen (O_2). Tropospheric ozone represents approx. one-tenth of total column ozone. The main source of tropospheric ozone is photochemical production by means of → hydrocarbons and → nitrogen oxides due to "smog mechanisms".

Tropospheric ozone has severe adverse effects (it is toxic for human beings, animals and plants; and enhances the greenhouse effect), whereas stratospheric ozone acts as a vital UV-B filter.

ozone-depleting potential (ODP)

The unit used to measure the relative ozone-depleting effects of chlorinated and brominated compounds. CFC-11 was chosen as a reference, and was therefore assigned the value of 1.

ozone hole

In 1985, it was discovered that, since 1977, ozone concentrations above Antarctica had been decreasing drastically during the months of September and October. Research conducted since then has shown that the annually recurring ozone hole is caused by industrially produced → chlorofluorcarbons.

ozone layer

A layer in the → stratosphere, at an altitude of between 15 and 30 km, where most atmospheric ozone is concentrated.

The ozone layer absorbs high-energy UV-B radiation, and transforms it into heat. Reductions in total column ozone density lead to increases in the intensity of cell-damaging UV-B radiation at the Earth's surface. Changes in the ozone layer can also affect the → climate. Industrially produced → chlorofluorocarbons (CFCs) increasingly deplete the ozone layer.

palaeoclimatic data

Climate-related data (e.g. temperature) from the Earth's geological past. Such data may stem from ice core analyses, samples of sedimentation taken from the ocean floors, or they may be based on annual rings of trees or on pollen analyses.

partial analysis

An analysis limited to a well defined section of the overall system under review. Interdependencies with the other system components should not be too pronounced, so that neglecting these components will not substantially impair the findings of the analysis.

partially halogenated CFCs

→ Chlorofluorocarbons.

pedosphere
The part of the Earth's surface that contains the soil layer where rock, water, air and microorganisms interact, and where soil-forming processes occur.

photochemical
Chemical reactions which occur in the presence of UV radiation.

photodissociation
A process in which molecules are split by absorbing electromagnetic radiation.

photosphere
The gaseous layer of the sun which emits the visible range of solar light.

photosynthesis
The process by which green plants use sunlight to build up carbohydrates from carbon dioxide and water.

phytotoxic substances
Substances which are toxic or harmful to plants.

plankton
Biocenosis of free-floating marine organisms with weak or no locomotor powers. Zooplankton: animal plankton; phytoplankton: plant plankton.

polar night
In the region between the poles and the polar circles, the time of year during which the sun remains below the horizon for over 24 hours. The duration of the polar night increases with latitude, lasting almost half a year near the poles.

precession
The gyroscopic movement of the Earth's rotation axis around the ecliptic, caused by the attraction of the sun and the moon. One full revolution takes approx. 20,000 years.

primary energy
Primary energy refers to the raw materials used to produce energy, i.e. primary energy sources are all natural energy sources such as → the fossil fuels (hard coal, lignite, petroleum, natural gas, oil shale, tar sand) and the nuclear fuels (uranium and torium), or the → renewable energy sources (e. g. hydropower, wind energy, solar energy, geothermal energy and biomass).

primary forest
Virgin forest; strictly speaking, a self-sustaining forest stand whose development has not been influenced by human activities at all, or only to such a limited

extent that its physiognomy has been shaped and determined by its natural environment.

radiation budget
The difference between the radiation absorbed and the radiation emitted (e.g. light, heat).

radiative forcing
Refers to forces within the climate system which act on the radiation budget of the Earth. The sum of all these forces determines the overall condition of the climate. A change in climate is induced by changes in the force of climate parameters.

radical
A molecule or an atom with unpaired electrons. Radicals are usually formed in the presence of ultraviolet light or heat, and are highly reactive.

radiometer
A satellite-borne instrument which measures the density of radiation from the Earth and from the atmosphere. Radiometers monitor radiation from satellite platforms in various regions of the spectrum, e.g. in the near-infrared range. They measure radiation density sequentially at all grid points of the Earth. The radiation density data are subsequently used to obtain the information desired (e.g. types and amounts of clouds, or types of land use).

reference model
A model used as a standard for purposes of comparison.

remote sensing
Remote sensing of the Earth's surface and its atmosphere refers to a process which indirectly derives the relevant parameters – such as the ocean surface temperature or the tropical forest stock – from images of emitted or reflected electromagnetic radiation. The equipment used for remote sensing operations includes not only → radiometers mounted on satellites, but also aircraft-borne cameras and radar units.

renewable energy sources/solar technology
The use of renewable energy sources is defined as the technical conversion of direct or indirect forms of solar energy, i.e. solar energy which has already been transformed in nature. Solar energy can be used to generate electricity by means of solar cells (photovoltaics), or to generate heat by means of solar collectors. Forms of solar energy which has been transformed in nature can be used as hydroelectric power, wind energy, geothermal energy, biomass, and ocean heat. The use of passive solar energy is defined as the conversion of solar energy

into heat directly in a building, or in wall structures connected with the inside of the building. Humanity's annual primary energy consumption, which currently amounts to approx. 90×10^{12} kilowatt-hours (or approx. 11 billion tonnes of coal equivalents), is only about one ten-thousandth of the solar radiation that reaches the Earth's surface each year. About 30 percent of the Earth's surface is covered by land, which means that the radiation reaching the Earth's land surface each year is 3,000 times greater than global primary energy consumption. Generally speaking, there is a vast technical potential for directly and indirectly utilising solar energy. If only a small percentage share of the Earth's land surface – i.e. several million square kilometers – was used in the long term to convert solar radiation into energy with an average total efficiency of 5 percent (including conversion, distribution and storage losses), and if at the same time, part of the technically usable potential of hydropower and wind energy was exploited, it would be possible to cover between two and three times the current global primary energy demand by means of renewable energy sources.

resources
Broadly defined, the term resources refers to all the inputs of labour, land (including raw materials and energy sources) and capital available for the production of goods. In a narrower sense, the term resources denotes raw materials and energy sources, with a distinction being made between resources that are non-renewable and those that are renewable. The latter, narrower definition has been applied in this report.

respiration
Refers to various biochemical processes which occur in plants. In all cases, it involves the use of the carbohydrates produced by photosynthesis for growth, nutrient absorption, and for sustenance and tissue replacement.

roughness
A measure of the resistance encountered by air currents as they pass over the Earth's surface.

savannah
Type of vegetation found in the → semi-arid tropics, where grassland is interspersed with solitary trees or groups of trees. With increasing moisture, the size of the tree groups increases, and savannah is gradually replaced by forest.

scenario
The prediction of possible outcomes, based on certain assumptions. Unlike forecasts, scencario predictions are independent of the scenarios, boundary conditions.

secondary energy
Secondary energy sources are all energy sources which result from conversion processes (e.g. in refineries or power plants) of → primary energy sources. Secondary energy sources include coal products such as coke and briquettes, petroleum products such as petrol and fuel oil, gas products such as city gas and refinery gas, as well as electricity and district heat.

semi-arid
A fairly dry climate where rainfall occurs within a period of three to six months.

sensitivity assessment
In this report: the assessment of the impact of various factors which affect the climate.

short-wave spectral range
The range of electromagnetic radiation between 0.2 and 4 µm.

soil erosion
The removal of soil by the action of water, ice, snow, wind and gravity.

soil moisture
The share of water in the entire soil mass.

solar constant (1,368 W/m²)
The flux density of solar radiation (radiative energy per unit of time and area) which reaches a standard area perpendicular to solar radiation, halfway between the sun and the Earth (150 million kilometers), at the outer boundary of the atmosphere.

solar cycle
→ sunspot sycle.

subsidiarity principle
A societal and socio-political principle according to which superordinate entities (e.g. countries) should carry out only those tasks which cannot be executed by subordinate entities (e.g. local authorities).

sulphur dioxide (SO₂)
Colourless toxic gas of pungent odour, developing mainly during the combustion of sulphur-based fuels (coal, oil), and to a lesser extent as a result of industrial processes.

sulphuric acid aerosol
The main component of the stratospheric aerosol layer (at altitudes of between 15 and 25 km). The ratio between sulphuric acid and water is 3 : 1.

summer smog
High level of air pollution which develops over conurbations under conditions of low air exchange intensity (e.g. during inversions). During summer smog episodes, not only toxic nitrogen compounds but also ozone are formed in the presence of solar radiation. The effects which this has on human health are primarily irritations of the eyes and of the airways.

sunspot cycle
Period of an average of about 11 years, during which the number of sunspots (areas where surface temperatures are lower than on the solar surface) found on the sun's surface goes through a cycle.

stratopause
→ Atmosphere.

stratosphere
→ Atmosphere.

succession
The replacement, caused by external factors, of one plant community by another at the same location.

sustainability
A term used in agriculture and forestry to designate management methods designed to ensure that the productive yield of an ecosystem is maintained undiminished for the benefit of future generations. The term is used somewhat inconsistently. Sometimes, it only refers to the preservation of forest areas, timber yields, the industrial value added, or the ecological equilibrium.

symbiosis
Co-existence of different forms of life to their mutual benefit.

synergy
Interaction; the condition in which the result of the action of two or more agents has a different quality than the sum of their individual actions.

terrestrial
Of, or relating to, land.

Third World
The term "Third World" is generally used to designate the developing countries. There are several explanations as to the origin of this expression. The most common one suggests that the world is subdivided into the First World (the West), the Second World (the East), and the Third World (the South).

trace gases
Gases of which only traces are found in the atmosphere, e.g. CO_2, N_2O, CH_4, CFCs.

transaction costs
Costs incurred during economic activities (e.g. exchange processes on the market) including the cost of collecting information, negotiating costs, the cost of hedging against risks, etc.

transpiration
The evaporation of water through the → stomata of plants.

tropics
Areas characterised by daily climate periodicity, i.e. the temperature variability between night and day-time is greater than between summer and winter, or between dry and rainy seasons.

tropopause
→ Atmosphere.

troposphere
→ Atmosphere.

ultraviolet radiation (UV)
Electromagnetic energy of higher frequencies or shorter wavelengths (below 400 µm) than visible light. UV radiation is subdivided into three regions: UV-A (320-400 µm), UV-B (280-320 µm) and UV-C (240-290 µm).

used energy, collectible energy
Used energy is defined as the energy which is actually used by the consumer, i.e. after subtraction of conversion losses involved in the utilisation of → delivered energy. Used energy includes heat, light, power and used electricity. Currently, approx. 45 percent of → end-point energy and about one-third of → primary energy are actually used in the Federal Republic of Germany.

validation
The process of verifying the validity or accuracy of, for example, the results of climate model calculations.

water vapour window
→ Atmospheric radiation window.

World Meteorological Organisation (WMO)

The convention establishing WMO was adopted at the Twelfth Conference of the Directors of the International Meterological Organisation in Washington, D.C., and entered into force on 23 March 1950.

WMO has the following tasks

- to facilitate international cooperation for the establishment of a network of meterological monitoring stations and meteorological service centres;
- to promote the development of systems permitting a rapid exchange of weather reports;
- to promote the standardisation of meteorological observation methods and to ensure the standardisation of published observations and statistics;
- to work for greater application of meterological findings in air traffic, shipping, agriculture and in other areas;
- to make proposals regarding research and training in the field of meteorology, and to provide assistance in the coordination of the international aspects of such programmes.

zonal

Running parallel to the circles of latitude.

List of Abbreviations

ALTENER	Alternative Energy: Community action aimed at making renewable energy commercially viable
BAHC	Biosphere Aspects of the Hydrological Cycle
BMU	Bundesministerium für Umwelt, Naturschutz und Reaktorsicherheit (Federal Ministry for the Environment, Nature Conservation and Nuclear Safety)
BMWi	Bundesministerium für Wirtschaft (Federal Ministry of Economics)
CBA	cost/benefit analysis
CFCs	chlorofluorocarbons
CHP	combined heat and power
CIS	Commonwealth of Independent States (formerly USSR)
DIW	Deutsches Institut für Wirtschaftsforschung (German Institute for Economic Research)
EASOE	European Arctic Stratospheric Ozone Experiment
EC	European Communities
ECE	United Nations Economic Commission for Europe
ECO/Fin	Council of the Economics and Finance Ministers of the European Communities
EFTA	European Free Trade Association
EPA	Environmental Protection Agency (USA)
EPOCH	European Programme on Climatology and Natural Hazards
FAO	Food and Agriculture Organisation of the United Nations
FCs	fluorocarbons
G&S	gas and steam
GATT	General Agreement on Tariffs and Trade
GCTE	Global Change and Terrestrial Ecosystems
GDR	(former) German Democratic Republic
GEWEX	Global Energy and Water Cycle Experiment
GFDL	Geophysical Fluid Dynamics Laboratory, Princeton/USA
GPCP	Global Precipitation Climatology Project

GWP	Global Warming Potential
H-CFCs	partially halogenated chlorofluorocarbons
HCs	hydrocarbons (organic compounds containing both carbon and hydrogen)
IAEA	International Atomic Energy Agency
ICSU	International Council of Scientific Unions
IEA	International Energy Agency
IGAC	International Global Atmospheric Chemistry Programme
IGBP	International Geosphere-Biosphere Project
INC	Intergovernmental Negotiating Committee
IPCC	Intergovernmental Panel on Climate Change
ISCCP	International Satellite Cloud Climatology Project
ISLSCP	International Satellite Land Surface Climatology Project
JGOFS	Joint Global Ocean Flux Study
JOULE	Joint Opportunities for Unconventional or Long-Term Energy Supply (deals with non-nuclear energy and energy efficiency)
MPI	Max-Planck-Institut fär Meteorologie, Hamburg
NASA	National Aeronautics and Space Administration
NCAR	National Center for Atmospheric Research (Boulder, Colorado/USA)
NMHCs	non-methane hydrocarbons
NMVOCs	non-methane volatile organic compounds
ODP	Ozone-Depleting Potential
OECD	Organisation for Economic Cooperation and Development (whose member states are the Western industrialised nations and Japan)
PAGES	Past Global Changes
R&D	research and development
SAGE	Stratospheric Aerosol and Gas Experiment
SAVE	Specific Action for Greater Energy Efficiency
STEP	Science and Technology for Environmental Protection
THERMIE	European Technologies for Energy Management
TOGA	Tropical Ocean — Global Atmosphere Programme
UN	United Nations
UNCED	United Nations Conference on Environment and Development
UNEP	United Nations Environment Programme

UNESCO	United Nations Educational, Scientific and Cultural Organisation
UV	ultraviolet radiation
VOCs	volatile organic compounds
WCRP	World Climate Research Programme
WMO	World Meteorological Organisation
WOCE	World Ocean Circulation Experiment
WWF	World Wide Fund for Nature

Units and Chemical Formulas

Chemical Formulas

Al_2O_3	aluminium oxide
CCl_3F	CFC-11
CCl_2F_2	CFC-12
$CClF_3$	CFC-13
$C_2Cl_3F_3$	CFC-113
$C_2Cl_2F_4$	CFC-114
C_2ClF_5	CFC-115
$CHClF_2$	chlorodifluoromethane (H-CFC-22)
CF_2BrCl	halon 1211
$CBrF_3$	halon 1301
$C_2F_4Br_2$	halon 2402
CCl_4	carbon tetrachloride
CH_3CCl_3	methyl chloroform
CH_3Cl	methyl chloride
CH_3Br	methyl bromide
ClO	chlorine monoxide
BrO	bromine oxide
HF	hydrogen fluoride
CO_2	carbon dioxide
CH_4	methane
N_2O	nitrous oxide
OH	hydroxyl radical
O^*	excited oxygen atom
CO	carbon monoxide
H_2SO_4	sulphuric acid
HNO_3	nitric acid
HCl	hydrochloric acid
SO_2	sulphur dioxide
SO_4	sulphate
NO	nitrogen monoxide
NO_2	nitrogen dioxide
C_xH_y	hydrocarbon
^{16}O or ^{18}O	oxygen isotopes with the molecular weights specified
Si_2O_2	silicon dioxide
MgO	magnesium oxide
O	atomic oxygen

214

Chemical Formulas (cont'd)

O_2	molecular oxygen
N	atomic nitrogen
N_2	molecular oxygen
H	hydrogen
Cl	chlorine
Cl_2	molecular chlorine
Br	bromine
F	fluorine

Prefixes and Symbols

pico	p	10^{-12}	one trillionth
nano	n	10^{-9}	one billionth
micro	μ	10^{-6}	one millionth
milli	m	10^{-3}	one thousandth
kilo	k	10^3	thousand
mega	M	10^6	million
giga	G	10^9	billion
tera	T	10^{12}	trillion
peta	P	10^{15}	quadrillion
exa	E	10^{18}	quintillion

Measures and Units

(a) Based on the International System of Units (SI)

meter	m	unit of length
second	s	unit of time
kilogramme	kg	unit of mass
Kelvin	K	unit of thermodynamic temperature
hertz	($1\ Hz = 1s^{-1}$)	unit of frequency

Derived units

newton	($1\ N = 1\ kg\ ms^{-2}$)	unit of force
pascal	($1\ Pa = 1\ N\ m^{-2}$)	unit of pressure [1]) or of stress
joule	($1\ J = 1\ N\ m$)	unit of work, energy and heat
watt	($1\ " = 1\ J\ s^{-1}$)	unit of power

---

[1]) In the meteorological service, $1\ mbar = 10^2\ Pa$ can also be used as a unit of pressure.

and:

1 m^2	unit of area
1 m^3	unit of volume
1 ms^{-1}	unit of velocity
1 ms^{-2}	unit of acceleration
1 kg m^{-3}	unit of density
1 m^{3}kg^{-1}	unit of specific volume

(b) Non-SI units

°C	degree Celsius (0 °C corresponds roughly to 273 K) Temperature differences are sometimes also given in °C (=K). The correct designation would be "degrees Celsius".
ppmv	mixing ratio: 10^{-6} = 1 part per million per volume
ppbv	mixing ratio: 10^{-9} = 1 part per billion per volume
pptv	mixing ratio: 10^{-12} = 1 part per trillion per volume
bp	years before present
Gt C	giga tonnes of carbon; 1 Gt C = 3.7 Gt CO_2

Energy Units and Conversion Factors

official unit: joule (J)[2])
1 joule (J) = 1 newton-meter (Nm) = 1 watt-second (Ws)

commonly used energy units:

1 terawatt-hour	= 1 tWh	= 1 x 10^9 kWh = 3.6 PJ
1 terawatt-hour	= 1 tWh	= 0.123 mn t CE
1 million tonnes of coal equivalents	= 1 mn t CE	= 29,308 PJ = 8.15 tWh;
1 exajoule	= 1 EJ	= 278 tWh

Conversion Factors

unit	kj	kWh	kg CE
1 kJ	–	0.000278	0.000034
1 kWh	3,600	–	0.123
1 kg CE	29,308	8.14	–

---

[2]) The joule has been the official unit of energy since 1 January 1978. The calorie (cal) and other units derived from it – such as coal equivalents (CE) and crude oil equivalents (COE) (1 CE = 0.7 COE) – can be used as supplementary units for a transitional period of time only.

216

List of Commission Documents

No.	Title	Date

1 **List of questions and experts** — October 1991
for the public hearing held by the Enquete Commission "Protecting the Earth's Atmosphere" on 25-26 Nov. 1991 on the topic of "Beitrag der Landwirtschaft zu direkt und indirekt wirksamen treibhausrelevanten Spurenstoffen in der Troposphäre und Auswirkungen"
(English translation "The Contribution Made by Agriculture..." filed under same document number)

Appointment of further experts

1-a **Statements submitted by the experts** — 14 Nov. 1991
on the list of questions (Commission Doc. 12/1) for the public hearing held on 25-26 November 1991

Contains statements by the following experts:

Prof. Dr. Meinrat O. Andreae,
Ralf Conrad
Dr. Isermann
Prof. Dr. Daniel H. Kohl
Dr. Lex Bouwmann
Prof. Dr. Sauerbeck + Prof. Dr. Haider (FAL)
Prof. Dr. Klingauf

1-e **Statements submitted by the experts** 29 Nov. 1991
on the list of questions (Commission
Doc. 12/1) for the public hearing held on
25-26 November 1991

Contains statements by the following
experts:

Prof. Dr. M. O. Andreae
Prof. S. K. Sinha
Dr. K. Isermann

1-f **Documents submitted by the experts** 29 Nov. 1991
Documents submitted at the public hearing
held 25-26 November 1991 by the following
experts:

Prof. Dr. M. O. Andreae
A. F. Bouwman
Prof. Dr. Fränzle
Dr. Isermann
Prof. Dr. D. R. Sauerbeck
Prof. Sinha
Prof. Dr. Söder
Prof. Dr. Scharpenseel

1-g **Statements submitted by the experts** 19 Dec. 1991
on the list of questions (Commission
Doc. 12/1) for the public hearing held on
25-26 November 1991

Contains the statement submitted by the
following expert:

Prof. Dr. Scharpenseel

2 **List of questions and experts** 11 Oct. 1991
for the non-public hearing held by the
Enquete Commission "Protecting the
Earth's Atmosphere" on 11 November 1991
on the topic of "Instruments"

3 **List of questions and experts** November 1991
for the public hearing held by the Enquete
Commission "Protecting the Earth's Atmosphere" on 28-29 January 1992 on: "Anhö-

rung im internationalen politischen Bereich über Willensbildung und Maßnahmen zum Schutz des globalen Klimas" (translations in English, French, Spanish and Russian are filed under the same number)

3-a **Statements submitted by the experts**
on the list of questions (Commission Doc. 12/3) for the public hearing held on 28-29 January 1992

20 Jan. 1992

Contains statements by representatives from the following governments and organisations:

Venezuela
World Bank
OPEC
IEA
Japan
Switzerland

3-b **Statements submitted by the experts**
on the list of questions (Commission Doc. 12/3) for the public hearing held on 28-29 January 1992

23 Jan. 1992

Contains statements by representatives from the following governments and organisations:

Norway
OECD
Poland
Egypt
Czechoslovakia
Netherlands

3-c **Statements submitted by the experts**   28 Jan. 1992
on the list of questions (Commission
Doc. 12/3) for the public hearing held on
28-29 January 1992

Contains statements by representatives from
the following governments and organisa-
tions:
   Argentina
   Algeria
   Indonesia
   Poland
   China
   Kenya
   Kirghiziya
   Japan
   Norway

3-d **Statements submitted by the experts**   3 Feb. 1992
on the list of questions (Commission
Doc. 12/3) for the public hearing held on
28-29 January 1992

Contains statements by representatives from
the following governments and organisa-
tions:
   World Bank
   Denmark
   Kenya
   Ukraine
   Egypt
   Mexico
   Indonesia
   Japan

3-e **Statements submitted by the experts**   5 Feb. 1992
on the list of questions (Commission
Doc. 12/3) for the public hearing held on
28-29 January 1992

Contains statements by representatives from
the following governments and organisa-
tions:
   IEA
   Sweden
   OECD

4-g **Statements submitted by the experts**   27 Jan. 1992
on the list of questions (Commission
Doc. 12/4) for the public hearing held on
16-17 January 1992

Contains statements by the following
experts:

Prof. Dr. Kohlmaier
Prof. Dr. Burschel
Prof. Dr. D. Sauerbeck
H. Oeschger, F. Joos, U. Siegentaler
Dr. Janz
N. Myers
GSF
Prof. Dr. Flohn
Prof. Dr. Kohlmaier

4-h **Documents submitted by the experts at the**   22 Jan. 1992
hearing
Documents submitted by the experts at the
public hearing held on 16-17 January 1992:

Dr. F. Arnold
Prof. Dr. Kenneweg
Prof. Dr. Burschel
Dr. Sauter
Prof. Dr. Schönwiese
D. D. Harvey
Dr. Lelieveld
R. Bojkov
Dr. Hekstra
Dr. Jäger
Dr. J. Fishman
Prof. Dr. Kohlmaier

4-i **Documents submitted by the experts at the**   20 Feb. 1992
hearing
Documents submitted by the experts at the
public hearing held on 16-17 January 1992:

Prof. Dr. P. Burschel
K. Janz

Summary of References

Andreae, M. O.: Statement presented to the Enquete Commission "Protecting the Earth's Atmosphere" at the public hearing "Agriculture I" held on 25-26 November 1991, Commission Document 12/1-e.

Bazzaz, F. A. and E. D. Fajer: Plant life in a CO_2-rich World, publ. in: Scientific American, Jan. 1992, pp. 68-74.

Berger, A.: The Milankovitch astronomical theory of paleo-climates: a modern review. Vistas in Astronomy, vol. 24, 1980, pp. 103-122.

Berz, G.: Klimaänderung und Versicherung. Report presented to the Enquete Commission "Protecting the Earth's Atmosphere" at the public hearing on "Recent Scientific Findings on the Greenhouse Effect and the Impact of Climate Change", Bonn, March 1992.

BMU (Federal Ministry for the Environment, Nature Conservation and Nuclear Safety): Beschluß der Bundesregierung zur Reduzierung der energiebedingten CO_2-Emissionen in der Bundesrepublik Deutschland auf der Grundlage des Zweiten Zwischenberichts der Interministeriellen Arbeitsgruppe "CO_2-Reduktion" (IMA); Bonn, 11 December 1991.

BMWi (Federal Ministry of Economics): Energie Daten '90. Entwicklung für die Bundesrepublik Deutschland. Bonn, December 1991.

Bolin, B. et al. (ed.): The Greenhouse Effect, Climatic Change and Ecosystems, 1986.

Bouwman, A. F.: Land use related sources and sinks of greenhouse gases. Present emissions and possible future trends. Land Use Policy, April 1990, pp. 154-164.

Bouwman, A. F. (ed.): Soils and the Greenhouse Effect, Wageningen, 1989.

Bouwman, A. F.: Statement presented to the Enquete Commission "Protecting the Earth's Atmosphere" at the public hearing "Agriculture I" held on 25-26 November 1991, Commission Document 12/1-a.

Bradley, R. S., Diaz, H. F., Eischeid, J. K., Jone, P. D., Kelly, P. M., and Goodess, C. M.: Precipitation fluctuations over northern Hemisphere land areas since the mid-19th century. Science, vol. 237, 1987, pp. 171-175.

Brown, L. R.: State of the World 1990. Norton & Co., N. Y. 1990.

Brunke, E.-G., Scheel, H. E., and Seiler, W.: Trends of tropospheric CO, N_2O and CH_4 as observed at Cape Point, South Africa. Atmos. Environ., vol. 24A, 1990, pp. 585-595.

BUND (Bund für Umwelt und Naturschutz Deutschland) (ed.): Der Verkehr — die unterschätzte Klimagefahr. Freiburg, January 1992.

Burschel, P.: Statement presented to the Enquete Commission "Protecting the Earth's Atmosphere" at the public hearing on "Recent Scientific Findings on the Greenhouse Effect and the Impact of Climate Change I" held on 16-17 January 1992 in Bonn, Commission Document 12/4-i, pp. 2-23.

Climate Action Network — UK: Sea Level Rise Impact — Special Report, publ. in: Hot News, issue 5, Winter 1992.

Coakley, J. A., Bernstein, R. L., and Durkee, P. A.: Effect of ship stack effluents on cloud reflectivitiy. Science, vol. 237, 1987, pp. 1020-1022.

Crutzen, P.; K. Heinloth: Oral statement presented by Mr P. Crutzen, expert, and by Commission member K. Heinloth at the public hearing "Agriculture I" held on 25-26 November 1991.

Crutzen, P. J.: Methane's sinks and sources. Nature, vol. 350, 1991, pp. 380-381.

Cubasch, U.: Zukünftige Klimaänderungsraten und die regionale Verteilung der Klimaänderung. Report submitted to the Enquete Commission "Protecting the Earth's Atmosphere" at the public hearing on "Recent Scientific Findings on the Greenhouse Effect and the Impact of Climate Change" held on 16-17 January 1992 in Bonn.

Del Genio, A., Lacis, A. A., and Ruedy, R. A.: Simulation of the effect of a warmer climate on atmospheric humidity. Nature, vol. 351, 1991, pp. 382-385.

DIW (Deutsches Institut für Wirtschaftsforschung): Entwicklung des Energieverbrauchs und seiner Determinanten in der ehemaligen DDR — Kurzfassung. Study commissioned by the BMWi (Federal Ministry of Economics). Bonn, July 1991.

Ebel et al.: Energiesparpotentiale im Gebäudebestand; Darmstadt, 1990.

Enquete Commission of the 11th German Bundestag on "Preventive Measures to Protect the Earth's Atmosphere": Protecting the Tropical Forests (2nd report), Bonn, 1990.

Enquete Commission of the 11th German Bundestag on "Preventive Measures to Protect the Earth's Atmosphere": Protecting the Earth — A Status Report with Recommendations for a New Energy Policy (3rd report), 2 volumes, Bonn, 1990.

Esser, G.: Modelling Global Terrestrial Sources and Sinks of CO_2 with Special Reference to Soil Organic Matter, publ. in: Bouwman, A. F. (ed.): Soils and the Greenhouse Effect, Wageningen, 1989.

European Community, ECO/Fin. Council: Protocol from the 1546th Council meeting; 16 December 1991 (draft); Brussels, 1991.

European Community, Directorate General XII: Cost Effectiveness Analysis of CO_2 Reduction Options (Synthesis Report); Brussels, 1991.

European Community, Commission: Communication from the Commission to the Council: A Community strategy for lower carbon dioxide emissions and more energy efficiency; Brussels, 14 October 1991.

European Community, Commission: Transport Market Europe, Commission of the European Communities, Directorate General Transport. Brussels, June 1991.

European Community, Council of the Environmental and Energy Ministers: Protocol of the 1544th Council meeting; 13 December 1991; Brussels, 1991.

European Community: Towards Sustainability: A European Community Programme of Policy and Action in Relation to the Environment and Sustainable Development (draft); Brussels, 1992.

European Community: The environment policy of the European Community: a report to the United Nations Conference on the Environment and Development; Brussels, 1991.

FAO: An Interim Report on the State of Forest Recources in the Developing Countries, Rome, 1988.

FAO: Bericht Nahrungs- und Getreideproduktion (report on food and grain production). No. 51-52, 20 December 1991.

FAO: Statement presented to the Enquete Commission "Protecting the Earth's Atmosphere" at the public hearing on "The Impact of Climate Change on Agriculture" held on 17-18 February 1992, Commission Document 12/5-e.

FAO: Statement presented to the Enquete Commission "Protecting the Earth's Atmosphere" at the public hearing on "Recent Scientific Findings on the Greenhouse Effect and the Impact of Climate Change I" on 16-17 January 1992 in Bonn, Commission Document 12/4-g, pp. 72-179.

FAO: The Forest Resources of the ECE-Region (Europe, the USSR, North America). Geneva 1983.

Flohn, H.: Wasserdampf als Verstärker des Treibhauseffekts. Report submitted to the Enquete Commission "Protecting the Earth's Atmosphere" at the public hearing on the topic of "The

Current Status of Scientific Findings on the Greenhouse Effect and the Impact of Climate Change" held on 16-17 January 1992 in Bonn.

Forum für Zukunftsenergien: Gutachten zum "Vorschlag für die gemeinsame Errichtung eines Sonnenkraftwerks von Industrieländern und einem Entwicklungsland im Sonnengürtel der Erde". Study commissioned by the Enquete Commission of the German Bundestag "Protecting the Earth's Atmosphere", working document 12/183. Bonn, March 1992.

Foukal, P., and Lean, J.: An empirical model of total solar irradiance variation between 1874 and 1988. Science, vol. 247, 1990, pp. 556-558.

Gaffen, D. J., Barnett, T. B., Elliot, W. P.: Space and time scales of global tropospheric moisture. J. Climate, vol. 4, 1991, pp. 989-1008.

GECR (Global Environmental Change Report): Fossil Fuel CO_2 Emissions Declined Last Year, Says Worldwatch. Vol. III., no. 24, 20 December 1991, pp. 5f.

German Federal Government: 5th Ambient Immission Control Report.

Gilliland, R. L.: Solar, volcanic and CO_2 forcing of recent climatic changes. Climat. Change, vol. 4, 1982, pp. 111-131.

Graßl, H., Jahnen, W., Hinrichsen, K., Englisch, G. and Hendel, S.: Methanquellen in der industrialisierten Gesellschaft, Max-Planck-Institut für Meteorologie, Hamburg, May 1991.

Graßl, H.: Klimaänderung durch Abholzung der Tropenwälder, publ. in: Entwicklung und Ländlicher Raum, H. 1/1992, pp. 7-10.

Graßl, H.: The influence of aerosol particles on radiative parameters of clouds. Idöjaras, vol. 86, 1992, pp. 60-74.

Häder, D.-P. and Worrest, R. C.: Effects of enhanced solar radiation on aquatic ecosystems. Photochem. Photobiol. 53, 717-725, 1991.

Haider, K.: Statement presented to the Enquete Commission "Protecting the Earth's Atmosphere" at the public hearing on "The Impact of Climate Change on Agriculture" held on 17-18 February 1992, Commission Document 12/5-b, 1992a.

Haider, K.: Statement presented to the Enquete Commission "Protecting the Earth's Atmosphere" at the public hearing on "Recent Scientific Findings on the Greenhouse Effect and the Impact of Climate Change II" held on 9-10 March 1992 in Bonn, Commission Document 12/6-a, pp. 2-38.

Halpert, M. S., and Ropelewski, C. F. (ed.): Climate Assessment. A Decadal Review 1981 — 1990. U.S. Dep. Commerce, National and Oceanic Administration (NOAA), Climate Analysis Center VII, 1991, 109 pages.

Hansen, J., Lacis, A., Rendy, R., and Sato, M.: Potential climate impact of mount Pinatubo eruption. Geophys. Res. L., vol. 19, 1992, (Pinatubo issue).

Harrison, E. F., Minnis, P., Barkstrome, B. R., Ramanathan, V., Cess, R. D., and Gibson, G. G.: Seasonal variation of cloud-radiative forcing derived from the Earth Radiation Budget Experiment. J. Geophys. Res., vol. 95 (D11), 1990, pp. 18687-18703.

Hekstra, G. P.: Statement presented to the Enquete Commission "Protecting the Earth's Atmosphere" at the public hearing on "Recent Scientific Findings on the Greenhouse Effect and the Impact of Climate Change I" held on 16-17 January 1992 in Bonn, Commission Document 12/4-b, pp. 57-68.

Hense, A., Krahe, P., Flohn, H.: Recent fluctuations of tropospheric temperature and water vapour in the tropics. J. Meteorol. Atmos. Phys., vol. 38, 1988, pp. 215-227.

Hofmann, D. J.: Aircraft sulfur emissions. Nature, vol. 349, 1991, P. 659.

Hofmann, D. J.: Increase in the stratospheric background sulfuric acid aerosol mass in the past 10 years. Science, vol. 248, 1990, pp. 996-1000.

Husar, R. B., Patterson, D. E., Holloway, J. M., Wilson, W. E., and Ellestad, T. G.: Trends of eastern U. S. haziness since 1948. Fourth Symposium on Turbulence, Diffusion and Air Pollution, January 1979, Reno, Nevada, Amer. Meteorol. Soc., pp. 249-256.

IEA (International Energy Agency): Climate Change Policy Initiatives: Update. Paris: OECD/IEA, 20 November 1991.

IEA (International Energy Agency): Written statement presented to the Enquete Commission for the international political hearing on the development of objectives and measures to protect the global climate held on 28-29 January 1992; Written Documents I, 20 January 1992; Commission Document 12/3-a.

IRRI (International Rice Research Institute): World rice statistics 1990. 1991.

Jäger, H.: Lidar observed trend in stratospheric background aerosol. In "Technical Digest on Optical Remote Sensing of the Atmosphere", vol. 18, Washington, D.C., 1991, pp. 153-155.

Jäger, H.: Stratosphärische Aerosole. Report submitted to the Enquete Commission "Protecting the Earth's Atmosphere" at the public hearing on "Recent Scientific Findings on the Greenhouse Effect and the Impact of Climate Change January 1992, Bonn.

Keeling, C. D., Piper, S. C., and Heimann, M.: A three dimensional model of atmospheric CO_2 transport based on observed winds: 4. Mean annual gradients and interannual variations. In "Aspects of climate variability in the Pacific and the Western Americas", D. H. Peterson (ed.), Geophys. Monograph, vol. 55, AGU, Washington, D.C., 1989, pp. 305-363.

Khalil, M. A. K., Rasmussen, R. A., and Shearer, M. J.: Trends of atmospheric methane during the 1960s and 1970s. J. Geophys. Res., vol. 94, 1989, pp. 18279-18288.

Khalil, M. A. K., and Rasmussen, R. A.: Atmospheric methane: Recent global trends. Environ. Sci. Technol., vol. 24, 1990, pp. 549-553.

Kimball, B. A.: Carbon Dioxide and Agricultural Yield: an assemblage and analysis of 770 prior observations: Water conservation laboratory report No. 14, November 1983. USDA, Agricultural Research Service, Phoenix, Arizona.

Kohlmaier, G. H.: Das Quellen- und Senkenproblem für atmosphärisches CO_2. Report submitted to the Enquete Commission "Protecting the Earth's Atmosphere" at the public hearing on "Recent Scientific Findings on the Greenhouse Effect and the Impact of Climate Change", January 1992, Bonn.

Kohlmaier, G. H.: Statement presented to the Enquete Commission "Protecting the Earth's Atmosphere" at the public hearing on "The Impact of Climate Change on Agriculture" held on 17-18 February 1992 in Bonn, Commission Document 12/5.

Kohlmaier, G. H.: Statement presented to the Enquete Commission "Protecting the Earth's Atmosphere" at the public hearing on "Recent Scientific Findings on the Greenhouse Effect and the Impact of Climate Change I" held on 16-17 January 1992 in Bonn, Commission Document 12/4-e, pp. 3-14.

Krause, F. et al.: Energy Policy in the Greenhouse, Vol II. The Cost of Cutting Carbon Emissions in Western Europe; 1992 (forthcoming).

Kuhn, M: Über die Entwicklung der Gletscher in den Alpen. Report submitted to the Enquete Commission "Protecting the Earth's Atmosphere" at the public hearing on "Recent Scientific Findings on the Greenhouse Effect and the Impact of Climate Change", March 1992, Bonn.

Lacis, A. A., Wuebbles, D. J., and Logan, J. A.: Radiative forcing of climate by changes in the vertical distribution of ozone. J. Geophys. Res., vol. 95 (D7), 1990, pp. 9971-9981.

Lenz, F.: CO_2-Effekte auf Pflanzen, publ. in: Huber, M. (ed.): Umweltkrise, Bonn, 1991, pp. 55-65.

Liu, S. C., McKeen, S. A., and Madronich, S.: Effect of anthropogenic aerosols on biologically active ultraviolet radiation. Geophys. Res. L., vol. 18, 1991, pp. 2265-2268.

Madronich et al., publ. in Geophys. Res. L., vol. 19, 1992.

Marchetti, C.; Society as a Learning System: Discovery, Invention, and Innovation Cycles Revisited. Technological Forecasting and Social Change, vol. 18 (1980), pp. 267-282.

Mather, J. H. and Brune, W. H.: Heterogeneous chemistry on liquid sulfate aerosols: A comparison of in situ measurements with zerodimensional model calculations. Geophys. Res. L., vol. 17, 1990, pp. 1283-1286.

Milankovic, M.: Kanon der Erdbestrahlung. Königl. Serb. Acad., Spez. Publ. 132, Sekt. Math. Nat. Wiss., vol. 33, 1941.

Myers, N.: Tropical forests, present status and future outlook, climate change, vol. 19, 1991, pp. 3-32.

Neue, H. U.: Statement presented to the Enquete Commission "Protecting the Earth's Atmosphere" at the public hearing "Agriculture I" held on 25-26 November 1991, Commission Document 12/1-b.

Nitsch, J.; Ziesing, H.-J.: Der Beitrag der Solarenergie zur Abwendung der Klimagefahren; Berlin, Stuttgart, 1991.

Norse, D.: Statement presented to the Enquete Commission "Protecting the Earth's Atmosphere" at the public hearing "Agriculture I" held on 25-26 November 1991, Commission Document 12/1-b.

OECD (Organisation for Economic Cooperation and Development): Written statement presented to the Enquete Commission at the "International Political Hearing Concerning the Formulation of Objectives and Measures to Protect the Global Climate" held on 28-29 January 1992; Written Documents II, 23 January 1992; Commission Document 12/3-b.

Oerlemans, J. and R. Warrick: Sea Level Rise, publ. in: IPCC-WG I: Climate Change — The IPCC Scientific Assessment, 1990, pp. 261-281.

Ozone Symposium: Ozon-Symposium, Munich, July 1991 (working document 12/74 of the Enquete Commission "Protecting the Earth's Atmosphere").

Patzelt, G. and M. Aellen: Gletscher. Bulletin no. 108 published by the Versuchsanstalt für Wasserbau, Hydrologie und Glaziologie der ETH Zürich, pp. 49-69, 1990.

Pitari, G., Visconti, G., and Rizi, V.: Sensitivity of stratospheric ozone to heterogeneous chemistry on sulfate aerosols. Geophys. Res. L., vol. 18, 1991, pp. 833-836.

Prognos: Die energiewirtschaftliche Entwicklung in der Bundesrepublik Deutschland bis zum Jahre 2010 unter Einbeziehung der fünf neuen Bundesländer. Study commissioned by the BMWi (Federal Ministry of Economics). Text edition. Basle, 20 December 1991.

Prognos: Wirksamkeit verschiedener Maßnahmen zur Reduktion der verkehrlichen CO_2-Emissionen bis zum Jahr 2005. Basle, 1991.

Raval, A., and Ramanathan, V.: Observational determination of the greenhouse effect. Nature, vol. 342, 1990, p. 758.

Rind, D., Chiou, E.-W., Chu, W., Larsen, J., Oltmans, S., Lerner, J., McCormick, M. P., and McMaster, L.: Positive water vapour feedback in climate models confirmed by satellite data. Nature, vol. 349, 1991, pp. 500-503.

Sagan, C., Toon, O. B., and Pollack, J. B.: Anthropogenic albedo changes and the earth's climate. Science, vol. 206, 1979, pp. 1363-1368.

Sauerbeck, D. R. and Haider, K.: Statement presented to the Enquete Commission "Protecting the Earth's Atmosphere" at the public hearing "Agriculture I" held on 25-26 November 1991, Commission Document 12/1-a, p. 280.

Sauerbeck, D.: Statement presented to the Enquete Commission "Protecting the Earth's Atmosphere" at the public hearing on "The Impact of Climate Change on Agriculture" held on 17-18 February 1992, Commission Document 12/5-a.

Scharpenseel, H. W.: Statement presented to the Enquete Commission "Protecting the Earth's Atmosphere" at the public hearing on "The Impact of Climate Change on Agriculture" held on 17-18 February 1992 in Bonn. Commission Document 12/5-a, pp. 60-81.

Schiffer, H.-W.: Energiemarkt '91. Primärenergie — Mineralöl — Braunkohle — Steinkohle — Erdgas — Elektrizität. Energiewirtschaftliche Tagesfragen, 42nd annual volume (1992), issue 3, pp. 154-174.

Schumann, U.: Air Traffic and the Environment — Background, Tendencies and Potential Global Atmospheric Effects. DLR, Bonn, November 1990.

Schumann, U.: Über den Einfluß des Flugverkehrs auf das Klima. Report submitted to the Enquete Commission "Protecting the Earth's Atmosphere" at the public hearing on "Recent Scientific Findings on the Greenhouse Effect and the Impact of Climate Change", January 1992, Bonn.

Sieferle, R. P.: Der unterirdische Wald. Energiekrise und Industrielle Revolution. Munich: C. H. Beck 1982.

Sombroek, W. G.: Do Soils matter ... at Global Change?, Wageningen, 1990.

Statistisches Bundesamt: Statistisches Jahrbuch 1990 für die Bundesrepublik Deutschland, Stuttgart: Metzler-Poeschel, September 1990.

Steele, L. P., Fraser, P. J., Rasmussen, R. A., Khalil, M. A. K., Conway, T. J., Crawford, A. J., Gammon, R. H., Masarie, K. A., and Thoning, K. W.: The global distribution of methane in the troposphere. J. Atmos. Chem., vol. 5, 1987, pp. 125-171.

Süddeutsche Zeitung: Entwicklungsländer treiben den Energieverbrauch hoch: Internationale Energieagentur: Bis zum Jahr 2005 Anstieg um 40 Prozent/ Rohölpreis mittelfristig bei 35 Dollar. Süddeutsche Zeitung, 3 June 1991.

Tans, P. P., Fung, I. Y., and Takahashi, T.: Observational constraints on the global CO_2 budget. Science, vol. 247, 1990, pp. 1431-1438.

Teramura, A. H., Sullivan J. H. and Ziska, L. H.: Interaction of elevated UV-B radiation and CO_2 on productivity and photosynthetic characteristics in wheat, rice and soybean. Plant Physiology 94, 1990, 470-475.

Toon, O. B., and Turco, R. P.: Polare Stratosphärenwolken und Ozonloch. Spektr. d. Wissenschaft, August, 1991, pp. 42-49.

United Nations Centre: Transnational corporations and climate change. New York 1990.

United Nations Environment Programme (UNEP): Environmental effects of ozone depletion: 1991 update.

Vaghjiani, G. L., and Ravishankara, A. R.: New measurement of the rate coefficient for the reaction of OH with methane. Nature, vol. 350, 1991, pp. 406-409.

Volz-Thomas, A., and Kley, D.: Ozone measurements in the 19th century: An evaluation of the Montsouris series. Nature, vol. 332, 1988, pp. 240-242.

WEC (World Energy Conference): 14th Congress of the World Energy Conference, Conservation and Studies Committee, Montreal, September 1989. Paris: Editions Techniques 1989.

Wege, K.: DWD-Observatorium Hohenpeißenberg, 1992.

Weidick, A.: Review of glacier changes in West Greenland. Zt. Gletscherk. Glazialgeol., vol. 21, 1984, pp. 301-309.

Weigel, H. J.: Statement presented to the Enquete Commission "Protecting the Earth's Atmosphere" at the public hearing on "The Impact of Climate Change on Agriculture" held on 17-18 February 1992, Commission Document 12/5-b.

Winiger, M.: Fragen zum Klima 2050. Auswirkungen von Klimaveränderungen auf Ökosysteme und Raumnutzung, publ. in: Huber, M. (ed.): Umweltkrise, Bonn, 1992, pp. 109-128.

Wissenschaftliche Mitteilungen der Bundesforschungsanstalt für Landwirtschaft FAL (Federal Agricultural Research Centre): Klimaveränderungen und Landbewirtschaftung part 1, special edition 117, 1990.

WMO/UNEP Global Ozone Research and Monitoring Project, no. 18, Geneva, 1989.

WMO/UNEP Global Ozone Research and Monitoring Project, no. 25, Geneva, 1992.

WMO/UNEP, Intergovernmental Panel on Climate Change (IPCC), 1990 .

WMO/UNEP, Intergovernmental Panel on Climate Change (IPCC), Supplement, 1992.

WWF (World Widelife Fund): Wie überlebt die Natur die globale Erwärmung/Can Nature Survive Global Warming?, Gland, 1992.

Zellner, R.: Atmosphärisches Ozon. Report submitted to the Enquete Commission "Protecting the Earth's Atmosphere" at the public hearing on "Recent Scientific Findings on the Greenhouse Effect and the Impact of Climate Change" held on 16-17 January 1992 in Bonn.

Zellner, R.: Ozonabbau in der Stratosphäre. Study conducted for the Enquete Commission "Protecting the Earth's Atmosphere" on the most recent findings of two measuring campaigns (EASOE, the ozone measuring campaign of NASA), Winter 1991/92.

Zwally, H. J.: Growth of Greenland ice sheet: Interpretation. Science, vol. 246, 1989, pp. 1589-1591.